Contents

Preface

Soil is a resource used by man and is a component of environmental systems. Thus it can be studied in terms of links between soil properties and process and other environmental components such as air, water, rock and life. In addition, the soil properties and processes which affect the use of soils by man are important topics for study. It is intended that this book should provide an introduction to these topics for the upper secondary levels of education and for introductory levels of higher education (colleges, universities and polytechnics). It is also intended for teachers who may already be specialists in other areas but who are relative newcomers to soil study. The book covers basic soil study and will therefore be useful to soil scientists, geographers, geologists, biologists, agriculturalists, ecologists and environmental scientists.

In this Second Edition we have taken the opportunity to broaden the scope of the book to make it applicable to various parts of the world. World soils is an extremely large topic and so the treatment of examples is necessarily selective. The examples selected are aimed at emphasising the major soil resources in the northern temperate lands, especially the more fertile glacial drifts and other soils used for arable cultivation, together with the deeply weathered tropical soils which form the basic resource of much of the more densely populated tropical areas. In addition, the problems of soil salinity are also discussed as they limit much of the potential use of soils in arid areas. The treatment of the principles of soil formation and properties is, however, aimed at covering many aspects applicable to world soils outside these more detailed case studies.

Chapter one deals with the fundamental processes involved in the development of soil. Chapter two examines the components of soil, their properties and the way in which these may combine to influence overall soil properties. In Chapter three, individual soil types are discussed. Chapter four discusses soil as a component of the ecosystem, dealing with the circulation and flow of nutrients, water and energy and with soil-plant relationships. Chapter five considers soil management and the evaluation of soil resources, Chapter six deals with the description and mapping of soil in the field and Chapter seven with a discussion of soil classification.

World soil classification is a confusing topic for the beginner: there are several different classifications in existence, often with different schemes in different countries. Moreover, it is often difficult to equate the terms of newer classifications with those of older ones. In this book, both older, established terms and soil classifications and the newer scheme of the United States Department of Agriculture (USDA) are covered in broad terms, using equivalent terms from other major classifications with cross-referencing to established older classifications where possible. Thus, the book provides an introduction to the principle soil groups and their major classifications; further details are discussed for selected areas only.

The book therefore attempts to impart the basic ideas of soil study, especially of components, interactions, processes, resources, description and classification. This will prepare the reader for more advanced texts where some of the complexities of interactions and classifications will be more apparent.

The authors are indebted to a number of individuals, especially former staff at the University of Bristol Geography Department, notably Len Curtis and Dingle Smith, as well as present and former students and staff of the Field Studies Council, especially Bob Troake, Maggie Calloway, Rob Lucas, David Job and Tony Thomas. FMC would like to thank former colleagues in the Soil Survey of England and Wales and at Manchester Polytechnic for their interest. STT would like to thank friends and colleagues for support, especially Lizzie Cole, Nigel, Bob, Adrian and Keith and many others, not forgetting Dave Briggs and also all the Sheffield Students who bought the First Edition. We would like to thank these and also all the other friends without whom we would have given up long ago, not least thanks to Catherine Courtney and our parents for so much help.

Frank Courtney
Stephen Trudgill

1

Soil development

1.1 Rock and soil

Rock weathering

Soil develops when rock at the surface of the earth is changed by a series of processes, collectively known by the term *weathering*. The rock is weathered and broken down by the combined action of water, gases and living matter. The formation of soil is not just a matter of the disintegration of rock; while the rock is disintegrating it is exchanging material with its immediate environment. A true soil is therefore a rock which has exchanged some material with its environment and the soil now incorporates not only rock but also water, gases and both living and dead organic matter.

Rocks and equilibrium

When rock breaks down to form soil it is tending to come into *a state of equilibrium* with its environment. By using the phrase 'a state of equilibrium' it is meant that an object is adjusted to the external forces acting upon it.

For example, if you were to place a beaker of hot water in a cold room then the water would cool until it was the same temperature as the room. The water would at that stage be adjusted to its external environment and would be in a state of equilibrium with the temperature in the room. Similarly one litre of hot water mixed with one litre of cold water would mix to produce two litres of warm water. In this case both items have adjusted to each other, resulting in a compromise.

The principle of equilibrium can be stated in a more general way:

matter tends to change by the loss or gain of energy into a form where energy differences between the matter and its environment (or between two sets of matter) are minimized.

Rock material deep inside the earth's crust is molten. This is an adjustment to the forces acting on the material. Nearer the earth's surface, rock is cooler and more crystalline. This is also an equilibrium adjustment to conditions.

Eventually, by earth movements or the erosion of the overlying rock, the piece of rock may find itself at the surface of the earth. The rock will have inherited characteristics from the place of its origin in the earth's crust, but it is now in a new environment at the surface. It is in *disequilibrium* with the new environment. That is, it is not in equilibrium with the conditions at the surface of the earth where cooler (and changeable) temperatures occur and where water, air and organisms are present. The rock has to adjust to the new conditions.

The adjustment can take many forms and may vary in the amount of time it takes, according to the nature of the surface conditions. In desert conditions the simple disintegration of rock occurs. The production of sand can be viewed as an equilibrium adjustment to harsh conditions. The rock cannot withstand the expansion and contraction caused by temperature changes, but the sand can expand and contract freely. Soil is not formed, however, because there is insufficient water and life to be incorporated into the disintegrated rock.

The material that disintegrates to produce the soil is called the *parent material*. It may be *igneous* rock, which had its source deep in the earth's crust as described above. It may be a *sedimentary* rock which has been formed from the deposition of previously weathered rock. Although these rocks have not been as deep in the earth's crust as igneous rocks and so have not become molten, they still inherit characteristics from the place where they were first deposited, for example in a fresh water or marine basin. As soon as they reach the surface of the earth they will start to alter, in response to the new conditions they have met. The third group of rocks are the *metamorphic* rocks, which are sedimentary rocks altered by heat or pressure. Also many soils in Britain are developed on *unconsolidated deposits* such as river alluvium or glacial drift. Again these deposits inherit characteristics from having been laid down under water or ice and when exposed at the surface begin to adjust to surface conditions and incorporate rain water, gases, organisms and organic matter to form soil.

The soil system

The approach adopted by systems analysis is extremely useful in the study of soil development. The object under study is termed the *system* and the workings of the system are divided into *inputs, outputs* and *internal processes*. Using this approach a soil can be studied in a similar way to a processing factory with raw material input, internal manufacturing processes and the output from the system (Figure 1).

In the case of the soil system, the system under study is the soil between the living plant above and the unaltered parent material below, whether this be igneous or sedimentary rock or an unconsolidated deposit. The inputs and outputs of a small area of soil (Figure 2) can be listed:

Inputs
1 Nutrients from decaying rock. (Nutrients are the chemicals used as plant food.)
2 Water from the atmosphere.
3 Gases from the atmosphere and the respiration of soil animals.
4 Solar energy. This provides energy to plants, thus controlling inputs in 5 and 6.
5 Organic matter from decaying vegetation and animals.
6 Excretions from plant roots.

Outputs
1 Nutrients taken up by plants.
2 Nutrient losses into water passing through the soil.
3 Losses of soil material by soil creep downslope. These may, of course, then form inputs to areas of soil downslope.
4 Evaporation.

However, the soil system is not a simple matter of input and output, and under natural conditions *recycling* will occur. For example, the nutrients lost as an output (output 1) may well return in leaf litter the following autumn (input 4). In this way many nutrients are recycled through the system. Obviously if the vegetation is removed by a crop the nutrient store of the soil will gradually be depleted until fertilizers will have to be added to the soil to replace them.

Movement in the system

The movement of *water* in the soil governs most of the processes in the soil. It governs the removal of

nutrients in drainage waters and the biological processes within the soil. It influences most of the *internal processes* of the soil, whether they be chemical, physical or biological.

Within soil, nutrients can be moved from their original positions, transported through the soil and deposited higher or lower in the profile (or vertical soil section). If the dominant water movement in the soil is downwards, as in regions of high rainfall and where the soil is very porous, the nutrients will be transported downwards in the profile. The loss of nutrients from the upper part of the soil downwards is referred to as *leaching*. The transport and deposition of various soil constituents to different depths in the soil leads to the formation of horizontal layers within the soil. These are termed soil *horizons* and can often be distinguished as differently coloured layers in a section dug through soil in a pit or roadside cutting. Further details of soil horizon distinctions are given in Chapter six and section 3.1.

1.2 Agents and processes of rock weathering and soil development

We have seen that soil is formed by the interaction of the soil parent material with its environment. But how does a parent material incorporate water, gases and organic material from the environment to form soil? This section looks at the processes which enable the equilibrium adjustments of parent material to take place. The soil-forming processes that result from the exposure of the material to water, air and life are considered in turn.

Processes associated with exposure to water

The most important process is that of dissolving. Associated processes are those of *hydrolysis* (the break down of minerals by water) and *hydration* (the incorporation of water into the mineral structure).

DISSOLVING
Materials *dissolve* into water to form a *solution* of the material. Dissolving (the verb to dissolve) is the process, and the solution (the noun) is the resultant product.

Before we can understand how solution processes work in the soil it is necessary to refer to a knowledge of basic chemistry. When a soluble material (the *solute*) comes into contact with water (the *solvent*) small particles of the solute move out from the solid into the water. This is the process

2

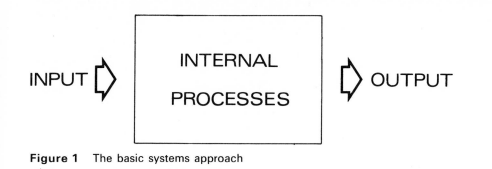

Figure 1 The basic systems approach

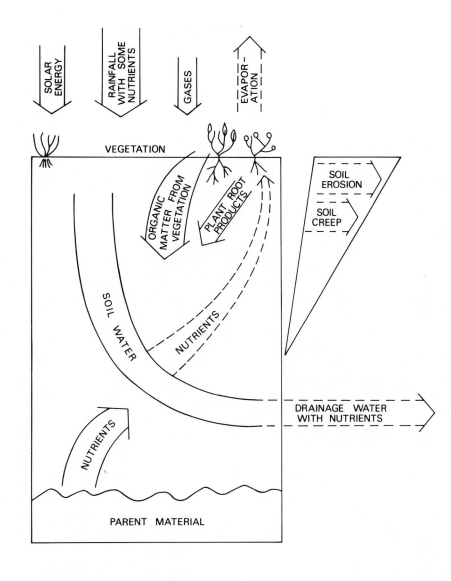

Figure 2 The major soil inputs and outputs

3

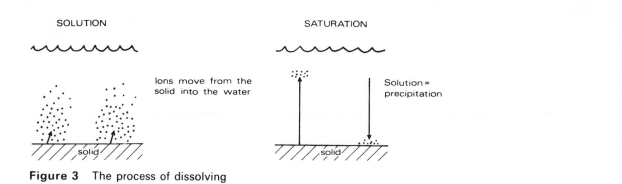

SOLUTION

Ions move from the solid into the water

SATURATION

Solution = precipitation

solid

solid

Figure 3 The process of dissolving

of simple *dissolving* (Figure 3). When many solutes dissolve they split up (or *dissociate*) into their constituent parts (though not all substances dissociate when dissolved and can exist as compound molecules in solution). These constituents are electrically charged and are referred to as *ions*. Common salt, for instance (sodium chloride), dissociates in water to yield separate sodium and chloride ions:

$$NaCl \longrightarrow Na^+ \text{ and } Cl^-.$$
$$ \text{cation} \quad \text{anion}$$

Sodium chloride in bulk is electrically neutral but dissociates to give *positively charged* sodium *cations* and *negatively charged* chloride *anions*.

Solute ions can also move back from the water to the solid and this is the process of chemical *precipitation*. Obviously, while the solid is dissolving the net movement of ions will be from the solid to the water. But at a certain stage it will be found that as many ions are moving from the water to the solid as are moving in the opposite direction. That is, precipitation equals dissolution. A state of equilibrium has now been reached; this is called *saturation*. The concentration of solute ions in the water at the equilibrium saturation state defines the *solubility* of the solute. Figure 4 demonstrates the amounts of various chemical elements found in soil water.

This basic chemical knowledge of the solution process can now be applied to the soil-forming situation. The constituents of the soil parent material will each possess a different solubility. The more soluble constituents will be easily washed away by rainwater and the least soluble will remain as the framework or skeleton of the soil. The formation of soil horizons, mentioned in section 1.1, is influenced largely by the solubility of soil materials. The more soluble chemicals are carried further down the soil profile while the least soluble chemicals remain undissolved in the upper layers of the

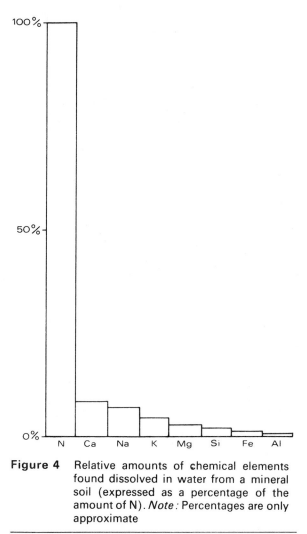

Figure 4 Relative amounts of chemical elements found dissolved in water from a mineral soil (expressed as a percentage of the amount of N). *Note:* Percentages are only approximate

soil. Rain water percolates through the upper layers of the soil, dissolving material slowly. Eventually the state of saturation will be reached and no further material can be dissolved. The materials are

4

then redeposited, or precipitated, lower down the soil profile (Figure 5).

It can be seen that the process of solution is an important way in which the minerals of the parent material of the soil react to the presence of water. Therefore the solubility of the soil parent material and the amount of rainfall (solvent) are important factors in the formation of soil, and an insoluble material will not break down easily to form soil, however much rain falls on it. Soluble material on the other hand will be readily moved in wetter areas, the degree of movement down the soil profile depending upon the amount of rainfall input to the soil.

HYDROLYSIS

Hydrolysis is the breaking down of minerals (in the parent material) by hydrogen ions and hydroxyl ions derived from water. Thus the mineral *combines* with the water rather than simply dissolving in it by dissociation. Some water in the soil exists in a partly dissociated state, that is the H_2O is already partly split up into H^+ and OH^- ions and the hydrogen ion (H^+) is particularly important in the attack of minerals.

In solutions of pure chemicals in the laboratory both H^+ and OH^- ions are involved in hydrolysis. For cations (M^+) the equation is:

$$M^+ + H_2O \rightarrow MOH + H^+.$$

For anions (X^-) the reaction is:

$$X^- + H_2O \rightarrow HX + OH^-.$$

Hydrolysis is thus the reaction of a solid ion with water to form an associated iron species plus H^+ or OH^-.

In natural situations complex minerals exist and hydrolysis is not as simple as in the above equations. Often both cation hydrolysis and anion hydrolysis occur together. Frequently cations in a mineral combine with OH^- ions from water and then the cations are replaced by H^+ ions later. An example of a complex reaction is that of microcline feldspar reacting with water.

$$KA1Si_3O_8 + H^+ + OH^- \rightarrow HA1Si_3O_8 + KOH$$

| microcline feldspar | dissociated water | hydrolysed mineral | potassium hydroxide |

The hydrolysed mineral containing the H^+ ion is unstable and usually breaks down.

Minerals composed of weakly ionised cations combine with OH^- of water more than with H^+ ions. Minerals composed of weakly ionised an-

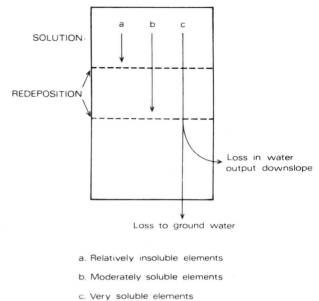

a. Relatively insoluble elements

b. Moderately soluble elements

c. Very soluble elements

Figure 5 Solution and redeposition in the soil profile

ions, such as the silica-rich minerals, take up H^+ ions from the water more than the OH^- ions.

An important factor in natural processes is that pure water rarely exists because it is usually dominated by hydrogen ions, H^+. These are derived from organic acids from decaying humus and the dissociation of carbonic acid in water:

$$CO_2 + H_2O \rightarrow \underset{\substack{\text{carbonic} \\ \text{acid}}}{H_2CO_3} \rightarrow H^+ + HCO_3^-$$

Plant roots and exchangeable hydrogen ions on acid clays also supply hydrogen ions. Thus in soil water containing much organic matter and many plant roots and acid clays the hydrogen ion tends to be the most important factor, leading to the dominance of mineral anion hydrolysis.

Many minerals that make up igneous and metamorphic rocks are rich in silica (SiO_2). The atoms in many silicate minerals are arranged in pyramids (called silica *tetrahedra*). These tetrahedra are held together by other atoms, especially calcium (Ca) or magnesium (Mg). The hydroxyl and hydrogen ions from water attack these atoms that link the tetrahedra and replace them with hydrogen ions. The silica tetrahedra which are linked by hydrogen ions are unstable and soon break apart. Thus the silicate minerals break down under attack from water which renders the minerals unstable (Figure 6).

5

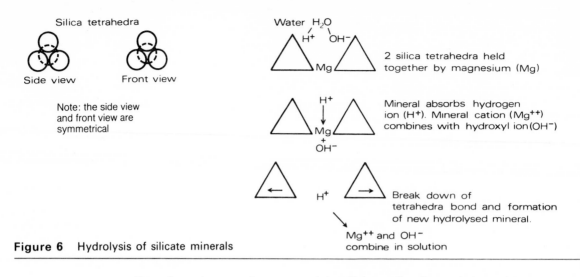

Figure 6 Hydrolysis of silicate minerals

Silica tetrahedra

Side view   Front view

Note: the side view and front view are symmetrical

Water H_2O

2 silica tetrahedra held together by magnesium (Mg)

Mineral absorbs hydrogen ion (H^+). Mineral cation (Mg^{++}) combines with hydroxyl ion (OH^-)

Break down of tetrahedra bond and formation of new hydrolysed mineral.

Mg^{++} and OH^- combine in solution

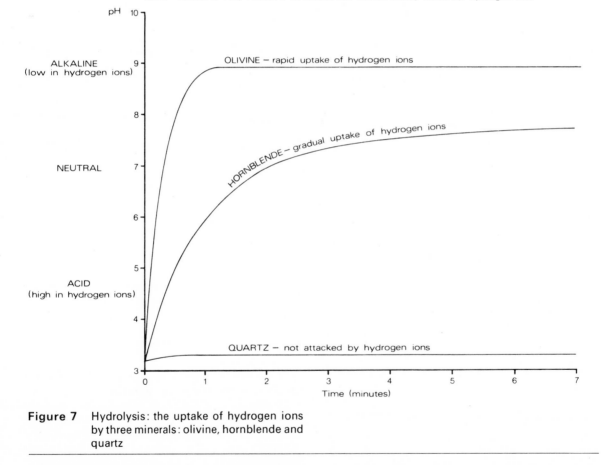

Note:– Quartz is very resistant to attack, but Olivine readily takes up hydrogen ions

ALKALINE (low in hydrogen ions)

OLIVINE – rapid uptake of hydrogen ions

HORNBLENDE – gradual uptake of hydrogen ions

NEUTRAL

ACID (high in hydrogen ions)

QUARTZ – not attacked by hydrogen ions

Time (minutes)

Figure 7 Hydrolysis: the uptake of hydrogen ions by three minerals: olivine, hornblende and quartz

It is possible to watch the process of hydrolysis occurring in a laboratory. If a silicate mineral is ground down to a fine powder and placed in water rich in hydrogen ions it is possible to measure the decrease in the amount of hydrogen ions in the water as they are absorbed into the mineral and caused the silica tetrahedra to break up. The concentration of hydrogen ions in water can be expressed in moles per litre hydrogen ions. A mole is the molecular weight in grams; for hydrogen this is 1, so 1 mole per litre = 1 gram per litre. Hydrogen ion concentration is often written thus: $[H^+]$, the square brackets indicating concentration. At neutrality there are $0.0000001 \, g \, l^{-1}$ hydrogen ions; since this is a cumbersome number, the logarithmic transformation, pH, is used. pH is thus defined as the logarithm of the reciprocal of the hydrogen ion concentration:

$$pH = \log \frac{1}{[H^+]}$$

The pH value of $0.0000001 \, g \, l^{-1} \, [H^+]$ is 7 and thus this concentration is equal to pH 7. pH 7 is neutral when H^+ ions are balanced by OH^- (hydroxyl) ions, values above this are alkaline and below this are acid. Using a pH meter or pH papers it is possible to detect a pH change from acid to alkaline as silicate minerals react with water and take up hydrogen ions (see Figure 7 and section 2.11).

HYDRATION

Some minerals can react to the presence of water by incorporating it directly into their crystal structure. The mineral anhydrite ($CaSO_4$), for instance, although not common in British soils, can occur in tropical soils and may be used to illustrate the process of hydration.

Anhydrite takes up water to form gypsum ($CaSO_4.H_2O$):

$$CaSO_4 + H_2O \rightarrow CaSO_4.H_2O.$$
anhydrite   water   gypsum

The uptake of water can alter the solubility of the minerals. In this example gypsum dissolves far more rapidly than anhydrite, taking fifteen days to reach saturation, whereas anhydrite takes thirty days to reach saturation.

Climate

While the nature of the parent material will be important in soil formation, the climatic conditions prevailing during soil formation will be equally important. In cold climates, the occurrence of freeze-thaw cycles will be important in the breakdown of rock masses. This breakdown provides a large number of surfaces for chemical processes to act upon. In hotter climates, thermal expansion and contraction of rock may have a similar effect. The amount of rainfall, or other source of moisture, such as dew, will also be an important consideration. Freezing and thawing of wet rock is a more effective process of rock shattering than is the freezing and thawing of drier rock. Similarly, thermal expansion and contraction of moist rock appears to be more efficient at breaking down rocks than is the expansion and contraction of dry rock. In addition, the movement of water through weathered rock masses and soil materials removes chemical weathering products in solution. In temperature and tropical climates the dominant movement of water is downwards. Weathering products are therefore moved downwards through the soil and rock material in solution, a process known as *leaching*. In semi-arid areas, the net direction of water movement often tends to be upwards because evaporation exceeds precipitation when measured on an annual basis. Here salts tend to be transported upwards through the soil and rock material, accumulating towards the surface and limiting the extent of chemical weathering. This process is known as *salinisation*.

Climates have often changed in the past, notably during the Pleistocene glaciations. During the glaciations, temperate latitude experienced a colder, more glacial climate than at present, with extensive ice sheets, while other mid-latitude areas, now arid or semi-arid, experienced a wetter climate. These legacies of climatic change have had a profound effect on soil formation and it is impossible to understand the nature and distribution of present soil resources without taking climatic change into account. In temperate latitudes, many of the deeper agricultural soils are developed from deposits of glacial drift. Evidence of disturbance by periglacial action is often seen – frost heaving and accumulation of soil material at the bases of slopes are notable examples. In currently drier climates, many of the soils can be thought of as developing during past, wetter periods, with less soil development at the present day. Many areas which are presently covered in saline soils were once areas occupied by former lake beds, the lakes having dried up during climatic change following the Pleistocene.

Temperature regime and moisture regime are thus two important factors in the weathering of rocks and in soil development; it should be emphasised, however, that because of climatic changes, not only current but also past climatic regimes have to be considered in order to gain a full understanding of the nature and distribution of current soil resources.

Processes associated with exposure to air

The most important process is that of oxidation.

7

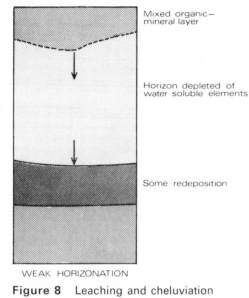

A) Simple leaching

Mixed organic–
mineral layer

Horizon depleted of
water soluble elements

Some redeposition

WEAK HORIZONATION

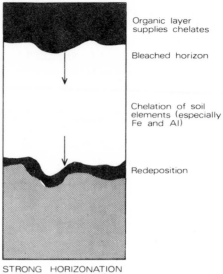

B) Cheluviation – leaching with chelates

Organic layer
supplies chelates

Bleached horizon

Chelation of soil
elements (especially
Fe and Al)

Redeposition

STRONG HORIZONATION
– very distinct horizons

Figure 8 Leaching and cheluviation

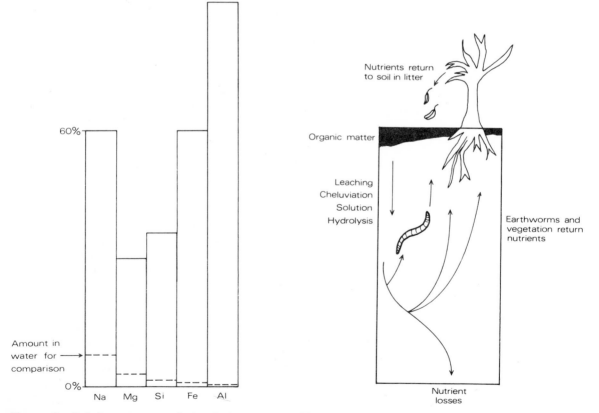

60%

Amount in
water for
comparison

0%

Na Mg Si Fe Al

Figure 9 Relative amounts of chemical elements
dissolved in water from soil rich in organic
acids (vertical axis as in Figure 4). *Note:*
Percentages are only approximate

Nutrients return
to soil in litter

Organic matter

Leaching
Cheluviation
Solution
Hydrolysis

Earthworms and
vegetation return
nutrients

Nutrient
losses

Figure 10 Nutrient movement in soil

Minerals in the soil parent material may take up oxygen from the atmosphere. This is a spontaneous reaction as the minerals are unstable in the presence of oxygen. Thus, when exposed to the air they spontaneously oxidize to achieve a chemically more stable form. This is, therefore, a good example of a mineral reacting to its new environment at the surface of the earth. Oxidation occurs as the mineral attempts to come into a state of equilibrium with its environment.

The characteristic brownish or reddish colours of most soils are due to the presence of oxidized iron. Ferrous iron (Iron II compounds) can be oxidized to ferric iron (Iron III compounds) which is red. In waterlogged soils, where air cannot easily penetrate, the soil is bluish or greenish. Here the colour comes from the unoxidized ferrous iron which is characteristically blue-green. Red mottles can be seen in some waterlogged soils where air has been able to penetrate (e.g. down old root channels) and oxidize the iron (see section 3.1).

Ferrous iron (Iron II) is much more soluble than ferric iron (Iron III) and because the former is present in waterlogged soils, iron is highly mobile under wet conditions. Iron may be precipitated, however, by contact with air or by changes in pH where acid waters lose their acidity. Iron may also be reduced and mobilised by organic compounds (see section 3.1). Iron may thus be mobile in wet, organic soils but be present in the insoluble ferric (Iron III) form under oxidising conditions. Insoluble iron oxide (Iron III compounds) often dominate tropical soils which have been strongly weathered under oxidising conditions for long periods of time. Such soils are to be found on very old land surfaces in parts of Australia, central Africa, South America, and parts of India and South East Asia. These soils are coloured red from the dominance of oxidised iron and various names have been given to these soils including oxisols, ferruginous soils and ferralitic soils (see Chapter 3).

Processes associated with exposure to plants and animals

The presence of life is critical to the formation of a true soil. If the environmental conditions are not suitable for plant and animal growth a true soil will not be formed. Plants and animals have two important functions in the soil formation processes:

1 They provide organic matter (through decay) which accumulates on the surface of the soil as a layer of humus. This organic matter has properties which influence the solubility of soil minerals.
2 Soil animals mix soil particles and help to aerate minerals.

It is very difficult to separate processes which are purely chemical from those which are biological in soil development. Usually biological processes have a profound influence on chemical processes. For example, an important process of soil formation and development is that of *chelation*. The word comes from the Greek word *chele* which means claw. The word aptly describes the process by which mineral ions are incorporated into the molecular structure of organic compounds. Elements like calcium, magnesium and iron are firmly attached in the molecular structure of organic compounds like humus acids.

If the soil has a thick layer of organic matter (humus) on its surface it means that any water percolating into the mineral material below will be charged with a large supply of organic compounds. Many of these compounds washed from the humus into the mineral soil below are capable of chelation. As the water percolates through the soil the organic compounds will take up mineral ions from the soil solids. In this way elements can be moved from the upper layers of the soil and washed down the soil profile. This washing process is termed *cheluviation*.

Cheluviation is responsible for the white, bleached layers which occur just below a layer of organic matter in some soil profiles (particularly in soils known as podzols). These bleached layers are extremely poor in nutrients as cheluviation is more efficient at removing elements than is the process of simple solution. Darker layers of redeposited organic matter and nutrients can be seen below these bleached horizons. These horizons are usually iron-rich, as iron is very easily moved by cheluviation (Figures 8 and 9).

As well as chelatory powers organic matter has the ability to produce hydrogen ions (which are important in hydrolysis). Thus the presence of organic matter on the surface of the soil greatly increases the movement of elements down through the soil profile.

Biological processes not only contribute to the movement of nutrients away from the surface of the soil but bacteria and fungi decompose the organic matter and release many of the nutrients that would otherwise be locked up in the organic compounds. These nutrients may then be available for use by plants. Also, the burrowing actions of animals like earthworms and ants may bring soil back nearer the surface and will thus bring nutrients which have previously been washed down the soil profile back to the surface (Figure 10).

Finally it should be emphasized that while we began this section with reference to a knowledge of simple chemistry, most of the processes in the soil are very complex. It is impossible to separate biological, chemical, atmospheric and hydrological processes in a soil. Each factor interacts to produce a complex mixture of rock particles, organic matter, water and nutrients that constitute a soil.

Summary

Soil can be viewed as the equilibrium product of the reactions of such materials as rocks, glacial deposits and alluvium with their environmental conditions. Chemical reactions, such as solution, oxidation, hydrolysis and hydration, occur as a result of the presence of water and air in that environment. Moreover, physical actions, such as freezing, may result from cold environmental conditions. The presence of life means that biochemical reactions, such as chelation, can take place and also that organic matter occurs. A soil is formed as a result of all these reactions. The soil becomes organized into horizontal layers, or horizons, as a result of leaching and of organic processes. Vegetation helps to offset leaching by the recycling of nutrients. Soil is thus a product of the soil parent material reacting to its environmental conditions through various chemical and biological processes taking place within the soil profile over time.

2

Soil components and soil properties

2.1 Soil material

What is soil made of? In order to understand how soil develops and to understand the inner workings of soil we must examine the separate components that make up soil. Also, in order to understand soil sufficiently to be able to manage it efficiently for agriculture we must understand how the soil components may react to different agricultural practices. Each component has particular properties and functions which influence how a soil behaves as a whole. We shall consider each component in turn: mineral matter, organic matter, water, air, biota (plants and animals) and nutrients.

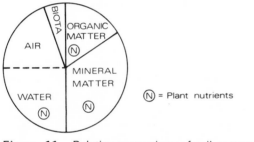

Figure 11 Relative proportions of soil components in an average agricultural loam

In sections 1.1 and 1.2 it was shown how the soil consists of a mineral 'skeleton' which is the weathered parent material. It was also shown that as the weathered material interacted with its environment it incorporated other components to form soil. In an average agricultural soil (a good, fertile loam) *mineral matter* from weathered rock and *organic matter* from plants and animals take up about half the volume of the soil and are thus the main soil components (Figure 11). *Air* and *water* take up the other half of the soil body. Air and water occupy the pore spaces between the mineral particles, and as water increases, with an input of rainfall, the amount of air decreases. As the soil dries (by evaporation and drainage) the amount of air in the pore spaces increases. Thus, in Figure 11 the boundary between air and water is drawn with a dotted line to indicate a fluctuating proportion. The

large *soil animals* and *plant roots* take up what would otherwise be air space. The *smaller biota* (bacteria, fungi and actinomycetes) are either present in the soil water or are distributed in the organic and mineral matter. *Nutrients* available to plants are found in the organic matter, in the soil water or in the mineral matter, but a large proportion is found in combination with compounds composed of both organic and mineral matter. These compounds are called the *clay–humus complexes* and they hold the biggest reserve of nutrients.

2.2 Soil mineral matter

Primary and secondary minerals

Soil minerals are derived from the minerals in the parent material by the weathering processes described in section 1.2. As soil formation is a continuous process the mineral matter can be conveniently divided into:

1 *Primary minerals* – those remaining unaltered from the original parent material.
2 *Secondary weathering products* – those produced by the weathering reactions.

While the primary minerals are those which were originally present in the soil parent material the secondary minerals are those which are produced in the soil. Thus the primary minerals remain in the soil during the soil-forming process and are those minerals which are relatively insoluble. They include such minerals as quartz, which are very resistant to weathering (see Figure 7). The secondary decomposition minerals include the products of the equilibrium reactions discussed in Chapter 1 and therefore include oxides and hydroxides of primary minerals which form as a result of exposure to air and water.

Clays

The exact composition of a clay depends upon the mineralogy of the parent material and the weather-

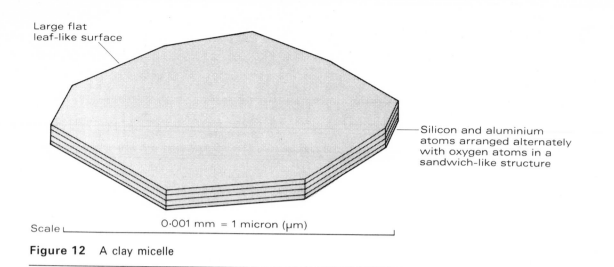

Large flat leaf-like surface

Silicon and aluminium atoms arranged alternately with oxygen atoms in a sandwich-like structure

Scale |___ 0·001 mm = 1 micron (μm) ___|

Figure 12   A clay micelle

ing environment. Silicate minerals, as was shown in Figure 6, may be prone to hydrolysis. One of the most important results of this reaction is the production of clays. Clays are minute particles composed of silicon (Si), aluminium (Al) and variable amounts of oxygen (O) and hydrogen (H) which are left after weathering reactions.

There are four main types of clay found in soils. Three, *kaolinite*, *montmorillonite* and *illite*, have a recognizable crystal structure. The fourth type, *allophane*, is non-crystalline and has no recognizable form. *Allophane* may include a number of different chemical types, but these are difficult to investigate because of the lack of structure; the terms the *Allophane Group* or the *Amorphous Clays* are often used to describe these clays. The first three types of clays mentioned have their atoms arranged in layers, like a sandwich. They belong to the group of silicate minerals termed *phyllosilicates* (*phyllo* = leaf-like) where sheets or leaves of atoms are laid down on top of one another. The basic clay structure is the *micelle* composed of several layers. The structure of a micelle is illustrated in Figure 12.

The three clay types are recognized by differences in their crystal structure, and these are shown in Figures 13–15.

a) ARRANGEMENT OF ATOMS

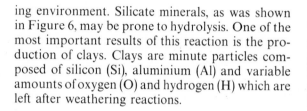

KEY TO ATOMS

● Silicon (Si)

⬤ Aluminium (Al)

○ Oxygen (O)

◍ Hydroxyl (OH)

b) DIAGRAMATIC REPRESENTATION

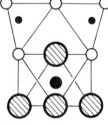

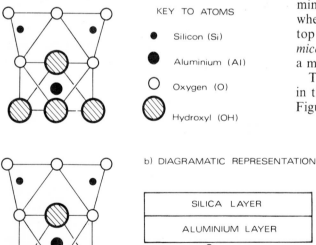

SCALE

| SILICA LAYER |
| ALUMINIUM LAYER |

⎤
⎥ 7·1 Å
⎥

$\overset{O}{\underset{O}{\overset{|}{\underset{|}{H}}}}$ BOND

| SILICA LAYER |
| ALUMINIUM LAYER |

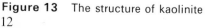

1 Angstrom unit (Å) = 1 x 10^{-8} cm

Figure 13   The structure of kaolinite

12

Kaolinite has one layer of silicon atoms joined to one layer of aluminium atoms by a row of shared oxygen atoms. This structure is then joined to the next silicon–aluminium layer by a bond consisting of hydrogen and oxygen (Figure 13).

Montmorillonite is similar except that it has an extra silicon layer in each unit. Thus the unit is a silicon–aluminium–silicon one. Moreover the units are joined by a weak water bond and not an O–H–O bond as in kaolinite (Figure 14).

Illite is almost identical to montmorillonite except that it has a very strong bond between the silicon–aluminium–silicon structure and this bond is made by potassium (K) (Figure 15).

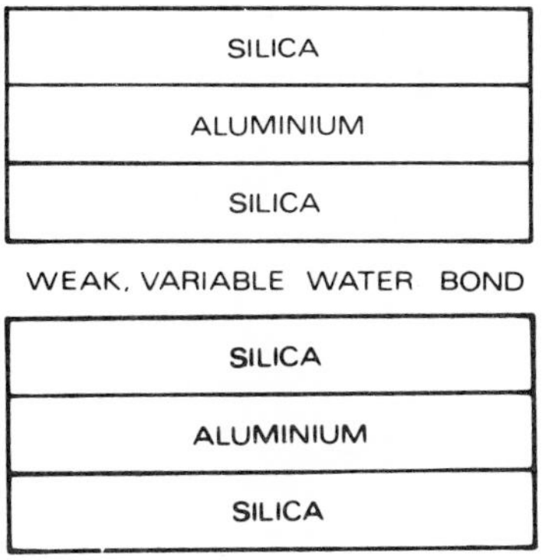

SILICA
ALUMINIUM
SILICA

WEAK, VARIABLE WATER BOND

SILICA
ALUMINIUM
SILICA

Figure 14   The structure of montmorillonite

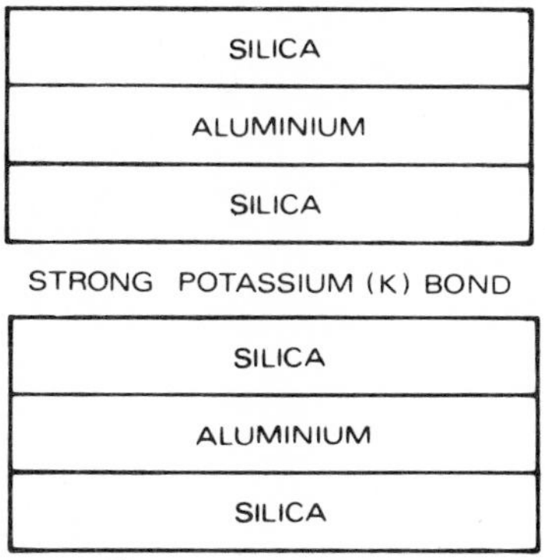

SILICA
ALUMINIUM
SILICA

STRONG POTASSIUM (K) BOND

SILICA
ALUMINIUM
SILICA

Figure 15   The structure of illite

2.3   Soil texture

Soil texture refers to the degree of coarseness or fineness of the mineral particles of the soil. These range in size from the large fragments of weathering rock down to the minute particles of about 1–2 microns in diameter. As the soil parent material may have been derived in a number of different ways and as weathering tends to break up the larger particles, a soil usually has a mixture of particles of different sizes. The relative proportions of the particles of differing sizes give the soil its texture.

The understanding of soil texture is a crucial step in the investigation of soil characteristics and soil behaviour as it influences many other factors, especially structure and the availability of water and nutrients.

A *coarse textured soil* has a high percentage of large particles of sand size and a *fine textured soil* has a high percentage of small particles, especially of clay. A *medium textured soil*, usually referred to as a *loam*, contains a mixture of coarse and fine particles together with intermediate, or silt-sized, particles.

It is possible to study the texture, or particle size, of a soil by rubbing a small, moist sample of soil between the fingers. Coarse particles of *sand* can be felt easily. *Silt* can be recognized by its soapy feel and a *clay* soil is pliable and can be moulded into various shapes. A clay soil can be rolled into long threads which do not break and also it stains the hands (often a brown or reddish-brown colour). A loamy soil can be moulded to some degree but the shapes easily break up. (The description of soil texture in the field is dealt with in detail on p. 95 and 96.)

While the above 'Field Method' of assessing texture is an extremely useful guide to soil type and behaviour, more precise information can be gained by the analysis of particle size in a laboratory. The particles are classified into groups of sizes (sand, silt and clay) and each class is separated by measurements of the diameter of the particles. Two classification schemes are often used, a so-called International scale and an 'American' scale, the latter derived in the United States.

Classification of the sizes of soil particles

Texture class	International scale (mm)	American scale (mm)
Coarse sand	2·0–0·2	2·0–0·25
Fine sand	0·2–0·02	0·25–0·05
Silt	0·02–0·002	0·05–0·002
Clay	less than 0·002	less than 0·002

As these scales use slightly different definitions of fine sand and silt it is important to state which scale is being used when texture results are being reported.

The amounts of soil in each size class are commonly determined by two laboratory methods: sieving and sedimentation. These techniques are described in detail in Appendix 1.

Sieving

In this technique sieves are used with meshes of varying sizes. Thus a sieve of mesh size 0·2 mm would allow fine sand, silt and clay particles to pass through, but would retain the coarse sand particles. A stack of several sieves is normally used, with the larger mesh sieves placed above the smaller meshes (Figure 16). The dried soil is poured into the top sieve and the whole stack is shaken on a mechanical shaker. The particles larger than any particular sieve mesh are retained by that sieve.

After sieving, the soil on each sieve is turned out on to a large piece of paper and the back of the sieve is brushed over the paper. A wire brush is used for the coarser wire sieves and a nylon brush for the finer nylon sieves. The soil on each piece of paper is carefully transferred to a labelled beaker and weighed. The result for the weight retained on each sieve is expressed as a percentage of the whole soil; for example, the table below shows the results for a 150 g soil sample.

Sieve mesh	Texture class (International scale)	Weight retained on sieve (g)	Percentage
0·2 mm	Coarse sand	80	53·3
200 µm	Medium sand	40	26·6
60 µm	Fine sand	10	6·6
PAN	Silt + Clay	20	13·3
	total	150	99·8

Sedimentation

Whereas sieving is least accurate at the fine end of the texture scale sedimentation is most accurate in the measurement of small particles. Therefore if both methods are used together a more complete soil analysis can be made than if one method is used alone. The Soil Survey of Great Britain use Sedimentation as the standard method for assessing texture.

In the sedimentation technique the dispersed, dried and weighed soil sample is poured into a column of water (Figure 17). The larger grains settle out almost immediately, but the smaller particles settle out very slowly. If the settling rate is measured it is possible to work out the size of the particles using *Stokes' Law* (first proposed in 1851), which states that *the settling rate of a particle is proportional to the square of the diameter of the particle.*

All the sand will have settled out from the top of the cylinder after about five minutes and the silt

14

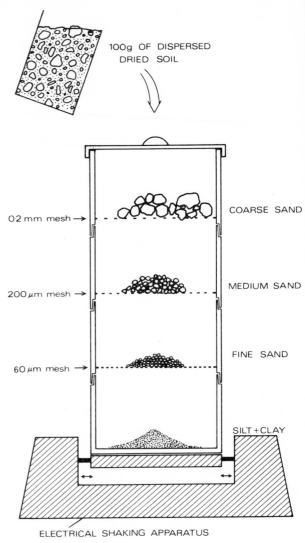

Figure 16 The principle of sieving

after about eight hours, the precise timing depending upon the temperature. There are two methods of assessing the rate of sedimentation:

1 using a hydrometer;
2 sampling with a pipette.

The *hydrometer* measures the density of the liquid. If there is a large amount of soil suspended in the water the density will be high and the hydrometer will ride high in the water. As particles settle out the hydrometer will sink.

Alternatively a 20 ml sample of the water can be drawn off with a *pipette* from 10 cm below the surface. The sample is carefully evaporated and the residue is weighed. (Accurate measurement is necessary as weight differences will be small.) This weight gives a measure of the solids still in suspension.

The results for texture analysis can be displayed on a pie diagram (Figure 18) or on a triangular graph (Figure 19). If the results given in Figure 18 are plotted on Figure 19 it can be seen how the triangular graph works, confirming that sample 1 is a clay loam, sample 2 loamy sand, 3 a clay and 4 a silty clay loam. Note that sand and silt have to

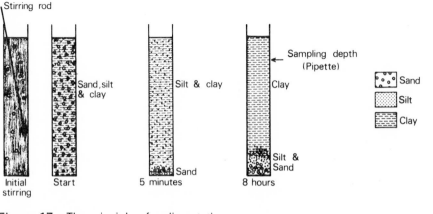

Figure 17   The principle of sedimentation

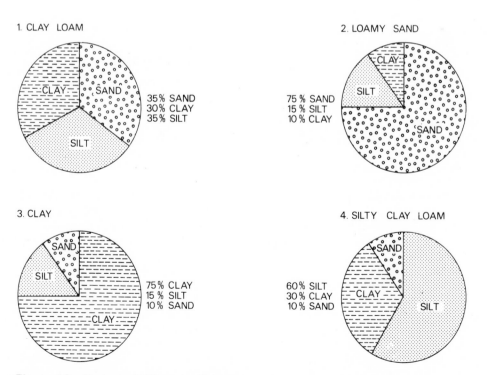

Figure 18   Texture of different soil types

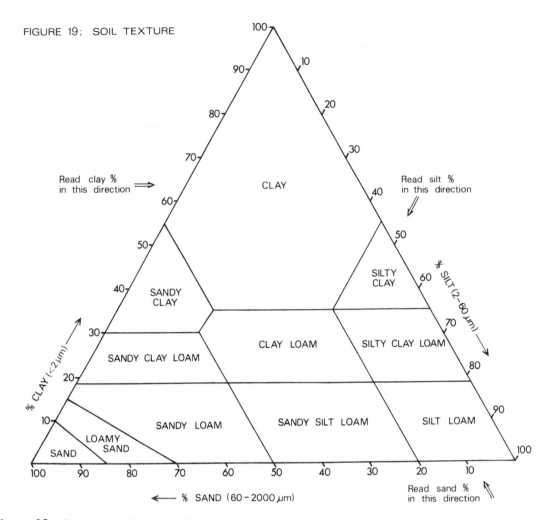

FIGURE 19: SOIL TEXTURE

Read clay %
in this direction ⟹

Read silt %
in this direction

CLAY

% SILT (2–60 μm)

% CLAY (<2μm)

SILTY
CLAY

SANDY
CLAY

SANDY CLAY LOAM

CLAY LOAM

SILTY CLAY LOAM

SANDY LOAM

SANDY SILT LOAM

SILT LOAM

LOAMY
SAND

SAND

⟵ % SAND (60–2000 μm)

Read sand %
in this direction

Figure 19   Soil texture (U.K. classification, 1976 system)

be quite pure in composition to be classed separately (bottom right and left hand corners), but that clay can have quite a large proportion of silt and sand in it. This is because the properties of clay are very dominating and soil reacts in a manner which is a result of the clay fraction even though quite a high proportion of the soil may be silt or sand.

A simple adaptation of the sedimentation technique is to pour soil into a beaker of water and stir it. If it is then left for a day or two, the particles will settle out, sand first, then silt, and finally clay. The depth of each type of particle can then be measured and calculated as a rough percentage to give a rough estimate of soil in each particle-size class.

Once texture has been assessed it is possible to make some statement about the properties of the soil as a whole. *Sand* particles impart to the soil a porous open texture, but contribute little in the way

of nutrients. *Silt* particles are usually smaller sand particles (e.g. of quartz), and similarly contribute little in terms of nutrients. Moreover they do not give a porous open texture, but the particles can be packed together, giving a dense soil. Some soils which are a problem to cultivate have a very high silt content. *Clay* soils on the other hand hold rich reserves of nutrients (see under soil nutrients, section 2.10). They are also noted for their properties of shrinking when drying and expanding when wet. The largest clays with the weakest micelle bonds expand and contract more than the smaller clays with stronger bonds. Thus montmorillonite is more expansive than kaolinite. It is the contraction of clays that causes soil to crack when it is dried.

Knowing the properties of each soil-texture component, it can be seen that the loam, with its mixture of sand, silt and clay, is in many ways the most desirable from an agricultural viewpoint. The sand

16

would give it a porous and well-aerated nature, the silt and clay would retain some moisture and the clay would hold nutrients in store. Conversely a soil composed of one dominant component would be difficult to manage. Purer clays tend to be rich in nutrients, but this is of little use to plant growth as the clay holds up water, giving a sticky, intractable, dense soil. The nutrient reserve may only be made use of by artificially draining the soil and also by improving the porosity and aeration of the soil by adding organic matter (or even sand though this is not a common practice).

2.4 Soil structure

Cultivation of many soils would be virtually impossible were it not for the fact that the individual

a number of small structures like breadcrumbs in shape and size; this is referred to as a *crumb* structure. Subsoils having tall and thin structure (*prismatic* or *columnar*) may aid the drainage of the profile as water can rapidly percolate down the sides of the structures. The types of soil structures are illustrated in Figure 20.

The type of structure is very much governed by the soil texture. In turn the overall properties of the soil (and therefore its value to agriculture) may depend greatly on the structures that are present.

How are the structures held together? Organic matter, chemical cements and clay play important roles. Of these, that of clay is the most important. Humus may help to stick smaller particles together as may the slimes secreted by earthworms and

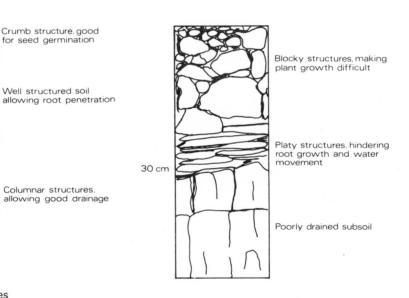

A) WELL STRUCTURED, USEFUL AGRICULTURAL SOIL

Crumb structure, good for seed germination

Well structured soil allowing root penetration

30 cm

Columnar structures, allowing good drainage

B) POORLY STRUCTURED SOIL OF LIMITED USE FOR AGRICULTURE

Blocky structures, making plant growth difficult

Platy structures, hindering root growth and water movement

30 cm

Poorly drained subsoil

Figure 20 Soil structures

particles making up a soil are usually aggregated into *soil structures*. Groups of clay, silt and sand particles are found stuck together in aggregates or structures (often referred to as *peds*) which have a profound influence on soil properties.

If it were not for soil structures the soil would have few pores through which air, water and plant roots could pass. Thus a compacted, structureless soil is of little value for agriculture as roots cannot penetrate, water is not available and the soil is not aerated. Soils with bad structures are often *layered* or *blocky* while a soil suitable for plant growth has

actinomycetes (see under soil organisms, section 2.9). Some nutrients in the soil can also act as cementing agents, especially calcium carbonate, and consequently a soil rich in calcium may have very well cemented structures (in fact in the tropics this may become too hard and the soil may set rock hard, forming calcrete). The cements used in the building industry are made from chalk and clay as raw materials.

While organic and chemical cements play important roles in forming structures a crucial process is that of *clay flocculation*. Clay particles can exist in

17

two states: *dispersed* and *flocculated*. Dispersed clay particles are separated from each other in individual 'coats' of cations, usually sodium. Flocculated clay particles are linked together by other cations, especially calcium, into clay aggregates or *floccules*. Dispersed clay soils are very dense and the particles are closely packed. This is why cultivation of saline soils, rich in sodium, is difficult; before cultivation can proceed the soil first has to be reclaimed by washing out of the salts, especially sodium chloride, from the soil. A practical example of this is found in the Netherlands where land reclaimed from the sea has to be leached with fresh water to remove the sodium salt and then treated with gypsum (calcium sulphate). In this case the calcium replaces the sodium coat round the clay and allows the clay particles to flocculate or stick together. When the clay is flocculated it forms larger particles, which give the soil a greater porosity but also retain the water-holding and nutrient-storing capacities of clays. Thus it is important to investigate the texture of the soil and its organic content and also the content of sodium and other nutrients, especially calcium, in order to understand soil structure.

We have already seen that texture may affect structure. Crumb structures are usually associated with loamy textures. Platy and columnar structures are found in clayey soils, although platy structures tend to be associated more with clay or silt soils where compaction has occurred. The columnar structures are formed by the shrinking and expansion of clays due to drying and wetting.

Ploughing can alter structures radically and this is the topic for discussion in section 5.2. Ploughing breaks up large, lumpy soil structures so that the soil is suitable for plant growth. However, this should not be carried out when the soil is very wet, especially on silt or clay soils prone to compaction, otherwise the structures may collapse completely. The weight of the tractor wheels may reduce the soil to a platy, compressed mass which is difficult to break up again later. Ploughing should therefore reduce the soil structures to a suitable size for seedling establishment and plant growth, but it should not damage and compress the structures so that plant growth is hindered.

2.5 Soil fabric

Soil fabric refers to the arrangement of soil particles on a very small scale, i.e. it is the small-scale soil structure. Soil fabric is studied by looking at the organization of a soil under the microscope. It is possible to study the microscopic structures of a soil in thin sections just as rocks are studied by the geologist.

18

In thin sections under a microscope the soil *plasma* can be recognized. This is the characteristic product of soil development, being a mixture of parent material and organic matter. It is an amorphous combination of humus, clays and chemical compounds (e.g. iron oxide), and is produced by the secondary weathering processes (see section 1.2) and by the incorporation of organic matter. The presence of organic matter distinguishes the soil plasma from the underlying mineral material, and the presence of mineral matter in the plasma distinguishes it from the overlying purely organic horizons. The characteristic of soil plasma is that *mineral and organic matter are virtually inseparable.* This is the result of the equilibrium reactions whereby the weathered rock reacts with its environment in an attempt to achieve a form which is stable in the presence of water, air and organisms.

Obviously it is necessary to solidify the soil in some way before it can be cut into a thin section. This is done by soaking the soil in a resin solution. The solution hardens on drying and forms a solid block. The resin block containing the soil can then be sliced into thin sections. The process of solidification is termed *impregnation* with resin.

Using impregnation methods much useful information can be gained about the minerals present in the soil. The primary minerals can be identified with little difficulty as they are similar to the unaltered rock minerals studied by geologists. The secondary, altered, minerals are usually more difficult – often being opaque and having no distinct outline.

If care is taken to impregnate the soil with resin carefully (while removing the air in the soil pores with a vacuum pump at the same time as the resin is introduced) the microstructures of the soil will be preserved in their natural orientation. In thin section the dark amorphous soil plasma and the pore spaces within and between the soil structures can be seen amongst larger sand grains (Figure 21). The pores of varying sizes have different functions (see also under Soil water, section 2.7).

Macropores – over 75 μm wide (0·075 mm): rapid transport of water and air
Mesopores – 75–30 μm wide: reservoirs of water for plants
Micropores – less than 30 μm wide: here the water is unavailable to plants

2.6 Soil organic matter

This is derived from decaying leaf litter and faecal material from animals. Sometimes the plant

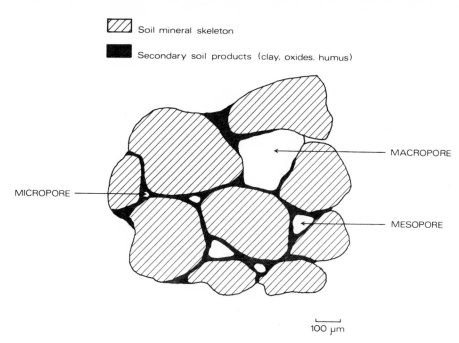

Soil mineral skeleton

Secondary soil products (clay, oxides, humus)

MACROPORE

MICROPORE

MESOPORE

100 μm

Figure 21   Soil pores

remains are still visible, but as the organic matter decays the *leaf litter* loses its structure and the individual leaves are no longer recognizable: *humus* has been formed. The term *humification* is used to describe this breakdown process from recognizable plant remains to an amorphous black or brown, almost jelly-like substance. Figure 22 illustrates the process of humification.

When the organic matter can be recognized as a distinct layer on top of the soil profile it is termed *discrete humus* because it is separate from the soil mineral matter. However, as humification proceeds the humus becomes incorporated into the soil mineral matter, especially to form *clay–humus complexes* in the soil plasma. It is then referred to as *intimate humus*.

In the soil profile three layers of discrete humus can often be recognized, the L, F and H layers:

L   leaf litter, leaves and other plant remains are recognizable;
F   the fermentation or humification layer, where decay is active;
H   the humus layer; plant remains are unrecognizable.

The H layer merges into the top layers of the soil where mineral and organic matter are mixed (see also section 6.5).

Whilst soil organic matter within *one* soil profile can be separated into discrete and intimate humus, when *different* soil profiles in different areas are compared three distinct types of discrete humus can be recognized. These occur in relation to the nature of the soil-forming environment and are called *mull*, *moder* and *mor*.

Mull is a soft, blackish material, crumbly when dry and rich in nutrients. *Mor* is a raw, fibrous, acid humus, poor in nutrients. *Moder* is an intermediate form.

Mull is produced by the action of fungi, bacteria and earthworms where the soil is not too acidic. It is common in lowland hardwoods (e.g. oakwoods), and in many fertile grasslands. Mor is formed in upland heath and bog environments which are wet and acidic and are not favourable for the activity of bacteria, fungi and earthworms. A mor-like mull, or moder, may be produced as a transitional state.

Since organic matter holds nutrients in reserve and since it can affect structure it is often important to determine the amount of organic matter in a soil in order to understand a soil's behaviour. One simple way of assessing organic matter in a soil is to weigh a small dry sample of soil which contains organic matter and to ignite it in a crucible in a muffle furnace. Details are given of the method in Appendix 2. The organic matter oxidizes and the resulting weight loss is used as a measure of organic matter content.

19

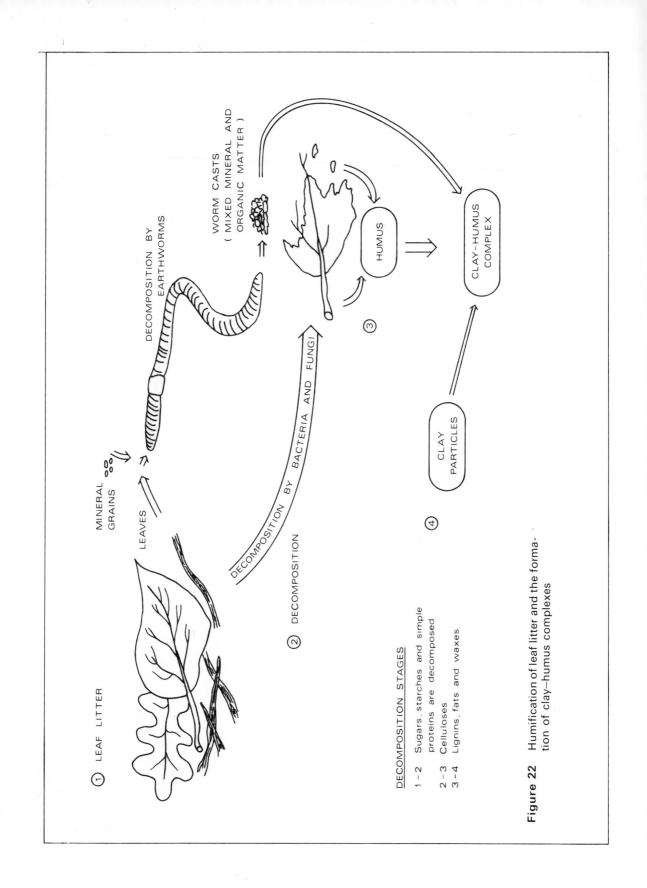

Figure 22 Humification of leaf litter and the formation of clay–humus complexes

2.7 Soil water

The amount of water (W) in a soil at any one time will depend upon the amount added by rainfall (R) minus the amount lost by evaporation (E), plant transpiration (T) and drainage (D). This relationship can be expressed in a mathematical way using the sign $\propto$ to indicate 'proportional to' thus:

$$W \propto R - (E + T + D).$$
$$\underset{\text{input}}{} \quad \underset{\text{output}}{}$$

The most important soil characteristic is the *water retention capacity*. Water may flow quickly through coarse, porous soils and not be retained or it may be retained for some time and be available for plant use. The latter is especially true if it flows

pores, but in the smaller pores water is held more tightly. The water may be held in a state available to plants in larger pores, but in smaller pores it may be held so tightly that plants cannot extract it.

The behaviour of water in a soil can be understood in terms of the forces acting upon it. Water is attracted to the solid soil particles by surface tension. Opposing this are the agents which exert forces away from the solid particles. These are the forces of gravity, the action of plant roots and evaporation.

The effectiveness of the force exerted by surface tension depends upon how far the water surface is from a solid particle. A thin film is held extremely tightly, but a thick film is held with less force, as shown in Figure 23. In the figure the water is shown

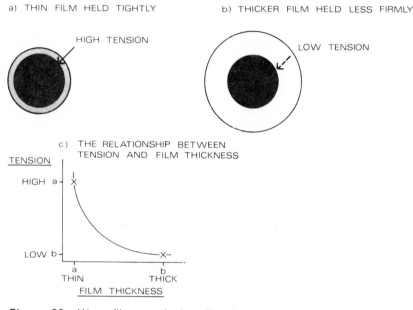

Figure 23 Water films on single soil grains

through tightly packed clay-rich soils. The availability for plant use is termed the *available water capacity*. Both the retention and availability of soil water depends upon *pore space*. As seen earlier this will depend upon texture and organic matter as these both influence structure and fabric (Figures 20 and 21).

Two pore space properties are important:

1 total pore space (soil porosity), and
2 the distribution of pores of different sizes.

Of these the second is the most important because pores of differing sizes have differing properties regarding soil water (see Soil fabric, section 2.5). Rapid water transport occurs in the larger

as surrounding a single grain to illustrate the point of how tension varies with film thickness. But in actual soils the grains are arranged to form pore spaces between the grains. It is the size of these pores which is the important factor. In a very small pore all the water will be near a solid particle, the surface tension will be very strong and the water will be tightly held. However, in a large pore the water will be further away from the solid particles, the surface tension effect will be lower and the water will be less tightly held. Indeed if a large pore is completely full of water the water will be held on to the particles only very lightly.

In the large pores where the surface tension effect is small, the forces exerted by gravity and plant roots may be greater than the surface tension. Thus water, instead of being held on to the particles, can be moved by the dominant force. This is why in section 2.5 the macropores transport water rapidly and why in the micropores the water is unavailable to plants. In these micropores, water is held so tightly to the solid that plants cannot exert enough suction to extract the water.

Water in a soil can be classified according to the

Water in soil is usually divided into three types according to its behaviour. Water held at less than $\frac{1}{3}$ atm and which can be moved by gravity is termed *gravitational water*. Water held fast in the soil, firmly adhering to the solid, is termed *hygroscopic water*. Between these states water is given the general term *capillary* or *matric water*. Matric is the American term and this type of water is water held in the soil matrix, or framework.

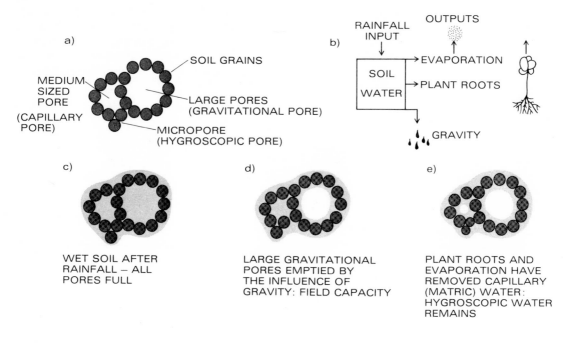

Figure 24 Behaviour of water in soil pores during drying

tension at which it is held in the soil. The tension is measured in atmospheres of pressure (atm) and the higher the figure the more firmly the water is held. Water in very small micropores close to solids is held at a tension equal to 10 000 atm. Evaporation can exert a suction of up to about 30 atm, plant roots can exert up to about 15 atm and gravity up to $\frac{1}{3}$ atm. The situation can be summarized:

water held at 30–10 000 atm: held tightly to grain surfaces in small pores

water held at 15–30 atm: moved only by evaporation; usually only moved as water vapour

water held at $\frac{1}{3}$–15 atm: water can be extracted by plant roots

water held at less than $\frac{1}{3}$ atm: water can be moved under the influence of gravity

From this division of water types we can divide soil pores into gravitational, capillary and hygroscopic pores. The classification of soil water and soil pores can be summarized:

1 *Gravitational water* – that water held in the large pores, possessing only a weak attraction to the solid. It is held at less than $\frac{1}{3}$ atm and can be moved under the influence of gravity.
2 *Capillary water (or matric water)* – The water held in medium-sized soil pores (in the capillary pores) at between 30 to $\frac{1}{3}$ atm.
3 *Hygroscopic water* – water held in very small pores, adhering firmly to the solid with a tension of up to 10 000 atm. (It may be removed artificially by 'boiling off' by heating the soil to 105°C.)

The types of soil water are illustrated in Figure 24 by considering a wet soil during drainage.

Soil water classification and plants

As plant roots can exert a tension of up to about 15 atm the water in a soil can be classified as unavailable (held above 15 atm) and available (less tightly held, at below 15 atm). Thus when soils dry out so that no water is left which is held at less than 15 atm the *wilting point* is reached. Only if the soil is wetted again will water be available to plants. After a rainstorm the soil may well be saturated with water. Assuming the soil is well drained, the gravitational water will soon drain off and when this has occurred the state of *field capacity* is reached. Water available to plants is that held between field capacity ($\frac{1}{3}$ atm) and wilting point (15 atm).

A method of measuring soil moisture content is given in Appendix 3.

2.8 Soil air

When the soil pores are not occupied by soil water they will be occupied by air. This soil air has a characteristic chemical composition and is different to the atmospheric air we breathe.

The living organisms in the soil produce carbon dioxide (CO_2) by respiration but do not use up carbon dioxide by photosynthesis as green plants do. Thus carbon dioxide builds up in the soil air and is present in far greater concentrations than it is in the open atmosphere. Carbon dioxide is also produced in the soil by root respiration and by the decay of organic matter. In the humification process (see section 2.6) organic carbon (C) is slowly oxidized to carbon dioxide (CO_2) by soil microorganisms. Figures for the composition of soil air show the chief differences – there may be as much as 300 times the concentration of carbon dioxide in soil air as there is in the open atmosphere:

	Oxygen content (O_2) (%)	Carbon dioxide content (CO_2) (%)
Atmosphere, normal composition	20·9	0·03
Soil air, average range	15–20	0·25–4·5

The carbon dioxide level may rise above the figures quoted, especially where soil porosity is low as in dense clayey soils and in wet weather.

Just as with soil water, soil porosity is a crucial factor in determining the amount and nature of soil air. The soil organisms, roots and decay processes all need oxygen to function. Also the processes all emit carbon dioxide. An 'open', porous soil with large pores allows the carbon dioxide to escape and the oxygen to enter by *gaseous diffusion*. In a soil with dense structures and small pore spaces oxygen cannot readily diffuse to aerate the soil, and carbon dioxide builds up in the soil. The *exchange* of gases is hindred and soil organisms do not flourish, roots do not grow well and decay slows down. Figure 25 contrasts well-aerated and poorly aerated soils. It can be seen that structure will have an important effect on aeration. Since structure affects drainage and water retention the water balance of the soil and the composition of soil air must also be closely linked. A soil with small pores will have increased water retention and decreased aeration while an open porous soil will allow rapid drainage and good aeration. Clearly, a soil with a mixture of small and large pores, as for example occurs in a crumb structure, will be the most advantageous for plant growth. Here some water will be retained in the small pores and aeration will be possible through the large pores.

The production of carbon dioxide shows a marked seasonal cycle. It is most rapid in warm, wet weather when root and microorganism activity are at their greatest (Figure 26).

2.9 Soil organisms

The various soil properties have different effects on soil organisms. Texture and structure are notably important in affecting the porosity of the soil, and therefore water retention and aeration, as described above, and these in turn influence soil floral and faunal activity. There are also soil processes and properties on which soil organisms have a considerable effect and these can be divided into three main groups of processes performed by soil organisms:

1 decomposition processes, e.g. humus decay, pesticide breakdown;
2 transformations and fixation, e.g. nitrogen fixation;
3 structural processes, e.g. aeration by earthworm burrows.

Decomposition

Soil organisms break down complex substances into simpler components. These may then in turn

23

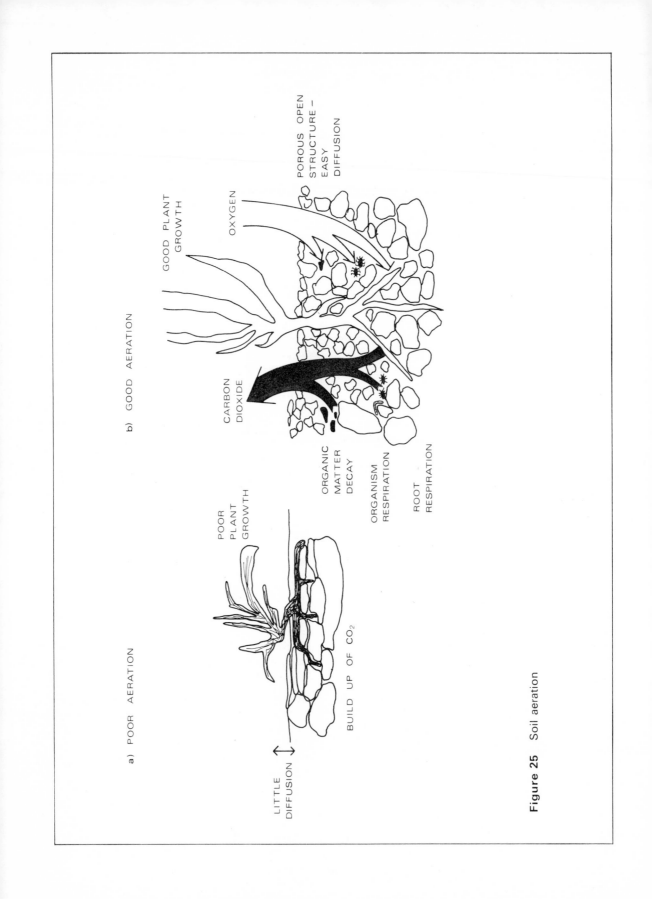

a) POOR AERATION

POOR
PLANT
GROWTH

LITTLE
DIFFUSION

BUILD UP OF CO₂

b) GOOD AERATION

POROUS OPEN
STRUCTURE –
EASY
DIFFUSION

GOOD PLANT
GROWTH

OXYGEN

CARBON
DIOXIDE

ORGANIC
MATTER
DECAY

ORGANISM
RESPIRATION

ROOT
RESPIRATION

Figure 25 Soil aeration

be synthesized into new soil components, three important examples being:

1 leaf litter to humus,
2 minerals to nutrients, and
3 herbicides and pesticides to simpler (less harmful) compounds.

Earthworms are important in transforming leaves into humus (Figure 22), whilst *bacteria*, *fungi* and *actinomycetes* are the main decomposers in the latter stages of the humification of organic matter. Actinomycetes are often classified with the fungi by biologists as they can be filamentous like fungi, but they can also resemble bacteria in being single celled. Thus they are a transitional group between the bacteria and the fungi. The activities of the organisms break down the organic matter, releasing organic and inorganic nutrients so that they are available again for plant use.

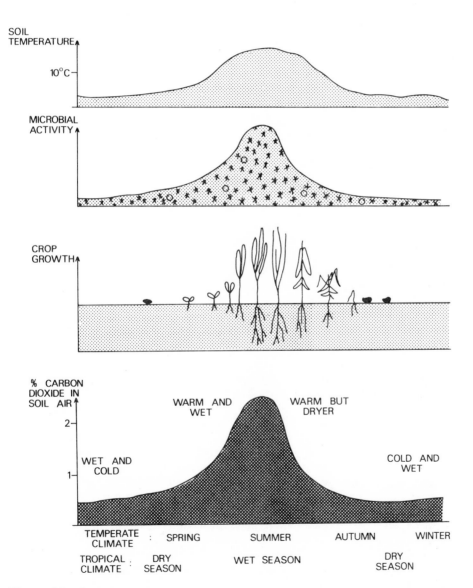

Figure 26 Seasonal carbon dioxide production

25

Fungi are the chief cause of decay of hard, woody, lignified tissue. The fungal threads, called *hyphae*, penetrate the woody tissue along the cell walls and excrete digestive enzymes (Figure 27).

Soil bacteria and fungi are able to 'attack' many soil minerals, either by producing acids which dissolve them or by directly utilizing chemical elements from the minerals in their metabolism. Their

ring of six carbon atoms) with chlorine and organic compounds attached. The bacteria attack the herbicide by cleaving off the compounds and chlorine from the benzene ring (Figure 28). Ninety per cent of the 2,4 D applied to soil may disappear in ten days by this process.

Other pesticides and herbicides are more resistant to attack by microorganisms. These may persist

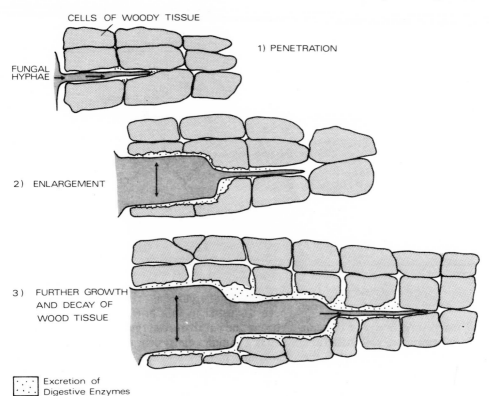

Figure 27 Wood decay by fungi

significance lies in the fact that they can attack resistant minerals, like some of the silicates, which are normally almost insoluble in rain water. Thus the nutrients derived from silicate minerals are made more readily available for plant growth by the decomposition of the minerals by bacteria and fungi.

Modern farming techniques require the use of pesticides and herbicides to control insects and weeds in order to promote agricultural productivity. A significant proportion of these applied chemicals may be left as a residue in the soil and here they may be degraded by soil organisms. For example, the herbicide 2,4 D (2,4 dichlorophenoxyacetic acid) is attacked by the bacteria *Achromobacta*, *Corynebacterium* and *Flavobacterium*. The basic structure of the herbicide is a benzene ring (a

in the soil and if so give cause for concern about their fate in the environmental system.

Transformations and Fixations

One of the most important plant nutrients is nitrogen (N). Soil microorganisms can fix gaseous nitrogen and transform it into nitrate, which can then be used as a plant nutrient. Nitrogen is the basis for all plant proteins and thus is a nutrient vital to growth. While these reactions will be considered in more detail in section 4.3 it will be useful to give an example of a transformation. Nitrobacter transforms *nitrite* (NO_2), which is toxic, to *nitrate* (NO_3), which is used as a plant nutrient:

$$2NO_2^- + O_2 \xrightarrow{\text{Nitrobacter}} 2NO_3^-.$$
$$\text{nitrite} \quad \text{oxygen} \qquad\qquad \text{nitrate}$$

26

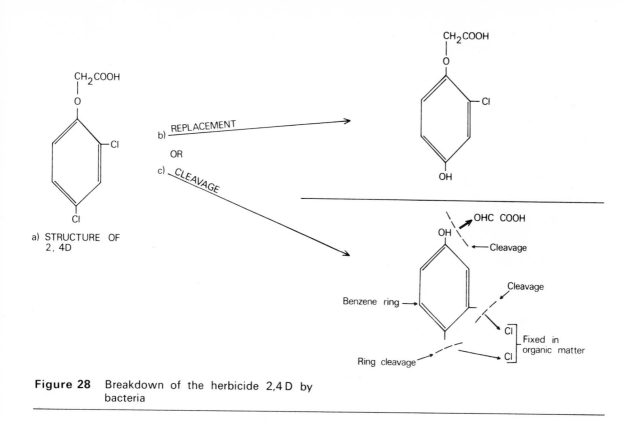

Figure 28 Breakdown of the herbicide 2,4 D by bacteria

Structural processes

Both the micro- and macro-organisms of the soil have a considerable influence on soil structure. Actinomycetes are thought to be important in the binding of individual particles together in crumb structures.

Earthworms, ants and small burrowing mammals are important in altering pore spaces as their burrows allow air and water to penetrate deep into the soil. Plant roots, when they die, also leave channels along which air and water may pass.

Summary	*The effects of soil organisms*
Decomposition	Bacteria
	Fungi
	Actinomycetes
	Earthworms
Fixation	Bacteria
Structural processes:	
Binding	Actinomycetes
	Fungi
Aeration	Earthworms
	Insects – ants, grubs, millepedes
	Burrowing mammals

Many other organisms exist in the soil than have been discussed in this brief section. Both herbivorous and carnivorous organisms are found. The soil is a complex ecosystem where no organism or inorganic process operates in complete independence. This theme will be discussed in greater detail in Chapter four.

2.10 Soil nutrients

Chemical elements found in the soil which are needed for plant growth are termed nutrients. Like soil water, they can be classified in terms of availability to plants (Figure 29):

1 Nutrients in solution in the soil water. These are freely available to plants, but may be washed out of the soil in gravitational water.
2 Nutrients attached to clay–humus complexes. These are the most important reserves as they are available to plants but are not easily washed out of the soil.
3 Nutrients stored in minerals and unavailable to plants unless released by weathering (e.g. by bacterial and fungal attack, see section 2.9).

As the most important reserve of nutrients is found in the clay–humus complexes of the soil

27

plasma it is useful to consider these complexes in some detail. Nutrients can be held in combination with humus substances and attached to the small clay particles. The clays have a *negative* electrical charge at their surface and to *balance* this electrically a layer of *positive* ions (or cations) coats the clay particles. These cations attached to the clay surface are referred to as the *adsorbed ions*. They are not

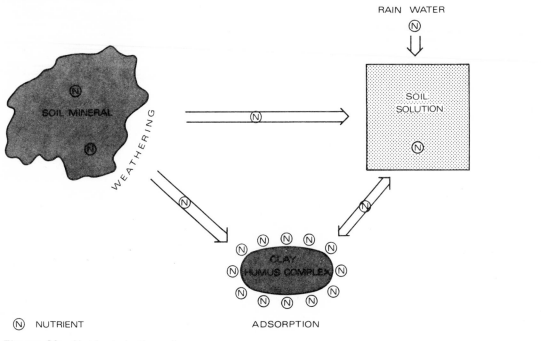

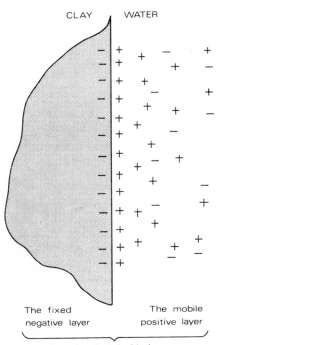

(N) NUTRIENT   ADSORPTION

Figure 29   Nutrients in the soil

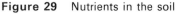

+ CATIONS

− ANIONS

The fixed
negative layer

The mobile
positive layer

The electrical double layer

Figure 30   Cations and anions at a clay surface

28

*ab*sorbed (incorporated in) but are *ad*sorbed (stuck) to the clay. The double layer of negative and positive charges was first described by *Gouy* and is referred to as the *electrical double layer* or the *Gouy Layer* and this is shown in Figure 30.

The amount of cations in the soil water next to the clay increases towards the clay surface and the amount of negative ions (anions) decreases towards the clay surface (Figure 31). The cations are the

Cation exchange

How do the nutrients become detached from the clay and move into the plant root? When a plant rootlet comes into contact with a clay particle with adsorbed cations the process of *cation exchange* occurs. Next to photosynthesis this is probably one of the most important processes in nature as it is the primary mechanism of plant nutrition. The root

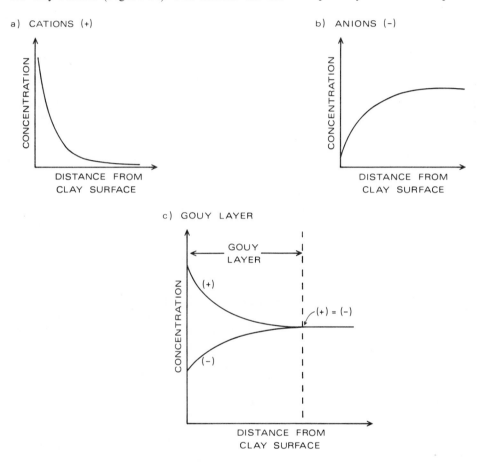

Figure 31 Cation and anion concentration at a clay surface

plant nutrients and include calcium (Ca^{++}), magnesium (Mg^{++}), potassium (K^+) and sodium (Na^+).

Calcium is important in the growth of shoot and root tips. *Magnesium* is a basic constituent of chlorophyll, an activator of plant enzymes and is involved in osmosis. *Potassium* is used in the formation and transport of starches, sugars and oils and also in enzyme reactions and osmotic processes. The role of *sodium* is not fully known, but it may fulfil some of the functions of potassium.

gives out hydrogen ions in exchange for nutrient ions (Figure 32). Calcium, magnesium, potassium and sodium can migrate from the swarm of cations adsorbed on to the clay surface and move to the plant root; their places are taken by hydrogen ions. The nutrient ions are translocated in the water-transporting xylem tissue of the plant to the stems and leaves. The hydrogen ions substituted on the clay surface are often used in the weathering of soil minerals. This releases further nutrient cations which can be adsorbed on to the clay surface.

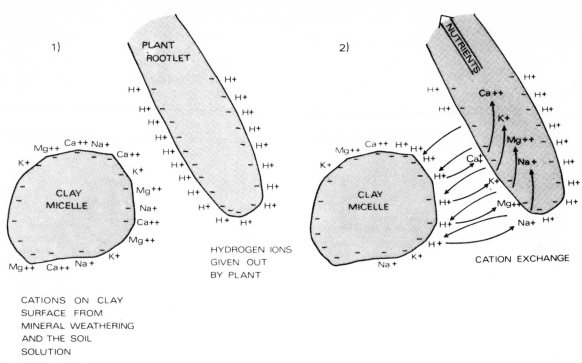

1)

PLANT
ROOTLET

HYDROGEN IONS
GIVEN OUT
BY PLANT

CATIONS ON CLAY
SURFACE FROM
MINERAL WEATHERING
AND THE SOIL
SOLUTION

2)

NUTRIENTS

CATION EXCHANGE

Figure 32 Cation exchange

The ability of clays and humus to yield cations for plant use is *called the Cation Exchange Capacity* (CEC). CEC is measured in milli-equivalents per 100 g of soil. A milli-equivalent is a measure of the ratio in which the element combines with or displaces hydrogen and is calculated by:

$$\frac{\text{molecular weight}}{\text{valency} \times 1000} \text{g,}$$

e.g. 1 milli-equivalent of calcium

$$= \frac{40 \cdot 08}{2 \times 1000} = 0 \cdot 02004 \text{ g}$$

The cation exchange capacity of humus is about twice that of pure clay, which emphasizes the importance of humus in soil fertility. The clay types discussed in section 2.2 differ in their cation exchange capacity, just as they do in their swelling and shrinking capacity (see under Soil structure, section 2.4). Their cation exchange capacity varies according to the surface area available for cation adsorption. Montmorillonite has the highest surface area, possessing both an internal and external surface. With illite the internal surface is already occupied by a fixed layer of potassium ions and therefore exchangeable cations are restricted to the outer surface and thus the CEC is less than that of montmorillonite. In kaolinite the CEC is even

30

lower as it has a much smaller surface area than the other clays (Figure 33).

While cations are readily stored in the clay–humus complexes, anions are less easily stored. Some anions are extremely important plant nutrients. They are, however, often readily leached as they tend to occur in solution in soil water rather than being adsorbed onto clay surfaces as cations are. This is especially true of nitrate (NO_3^-). Nitrate is therefore often added to the soil in fertilizer or organic matter to offset leaching losses (see section 5.1).

2.11   Soil acidity or pH

Soil pH is a measure of the concentration of the hydrogen ions in the soil water. Since an acid is a compound which dissociates (see section 1.2) in water to yield hydrogen ions (H^+), soil pH is a measure of the acidity of the soil water. Soil acidity is an important factor in the availability of plant nutrients.

Many chemical compounds found in soil are most soluble when they are in a slightly acidic solution, i.e. one charged with hydrogen ions. When the elements are most soluble they are at their most available for plants to take up and use. Thus there is an optimum pH for plant growth and this is when

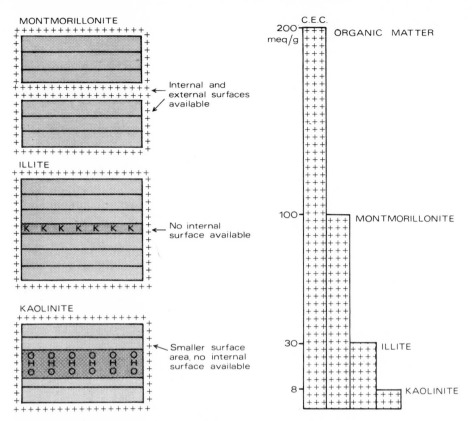

Figure 33 Cation exchange capacity

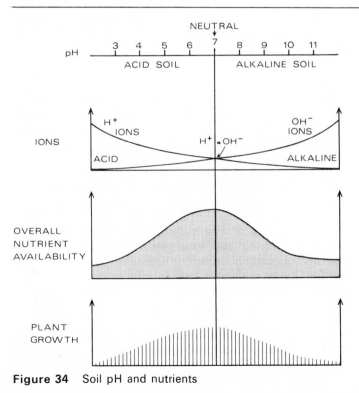

Figure 34 Soil pH and nutrients

the pH is slightly acid. In Britain soils tend to be rather more acid than this optimum and the chemical compounds may be so soluble as to be toxic. The addition of lime brings the pH up to the optimum for plant growth. The liming problem is discussed further in section 5.1.

pH is described on pp. 6–7. Liming has the effect of raising pH. Lime (calcium carbonate) reacts with H^+ ions adsorbed onto clays, leaving Ca^{2+}

Summary
Soil minerals, texture, structure, fabric, organic matter, water, air, organisms, nutrients and pH have been discussed. It has become apparent that many of these soil components and properties are related. These relationships are summarized in Figure 35.

Starting with soil minerals these will influence nutrient status and texture according to grain com-

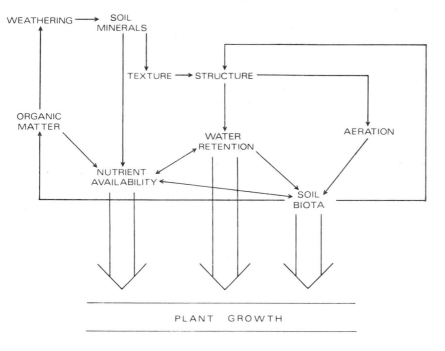

Figure 35   Summary of soil factors discussed

ions adsorbed onto clays and producing water and carbon dioxide thus:

$$CaCO_3 + 2H^+ \boxed{clay} \rightarrow Ca^{2+} \boxed{clay} + H_2O + CO_2$$

Similar replacement of calcium on clays will occur if lime is added as calcium oxide (CaO) or calcium hydroxide $(Ca(OH)_2)$, though the products will differ.

The relationship between soil pH, general nutrient availability and plant growth are shown in Figure 34. Plant growth is generally at an optimum around pH 6.5 – 7, though this varies with individual species (see p. 66-67). Liming therefore aims to bring pH up to these values if a soil is highly acid.

position, and the proportions of secondary and primary minerals. Texture will affect structure, controlling water retention and aeration. These are two important controls of soil organisms which in turn influence the nature of the soil humus as well as soil structure. Organic matter influences nutrient availability as does mineral type and water retention. All these factors interact to influence plant growth.

It is emphasized that the soil is a complex system where factors are interdependent and no factor, biological or physical, operates in complete independence.

3

Soil types and their development

3.1 Soil processes and the development of soil types

The formation of soil horizons

Soils can be divided into soil types largely on the basis of the horizontal layers or *horizons* which are visible when a pit is dug into the soil. These horizons are a result of the soil development processes discussed in sections 1.1 and 1.2: weathering and oxidation of minerals, leaching, salinisation, cheluviation and the accumulation of humus.

The horizons are differentiated in detail by several variables, the main ones being colour, texture, organic content, structure, stoniness,

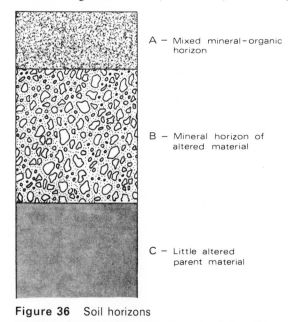

A – Mixed mineral-organic horizon

B – Mineral horizon of altered material

C – Little altered parent material

Figure 36 Soil horizons

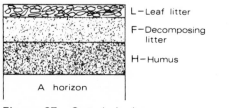

L – Leaf litter
F – Decomposing litter
H – Humus
A horizon

Figure 37 Organic horizons

acidity and nutrient content (see section 6.5). The major divisions in the soil profile are the A, B and C horizons (Figure 36). The *A horizon* is that of organic accumulation and is composed of leaf litter which is decaying and mixing with the underlying mineral soil. Immediately above the A horizon may be one or several of the L, F and H horizons referred to in section 2.6 (Figure 37). The separate A horizon is the mixed mineral–organic layer beneath the H horizon. Below the A horizon is the mineral *B horizon*, with a minimal organic content. The mineral matter is weathered and this distinguishes it from the unweathered parent material below, the *C horizon*.

Each horizon may be subdivided according to its precise nature and it is the formation of individual, distinctive horizons that gives each soil type its characteristic nature (see p. 91).

Soil types are classified on the basis of the horizons which can be recognised in the soil *profile*. The profile is defined as a two dimensional vertical section of soil. However, the United States Department of Agriculture (USDA) classify soils on the basis of the *pedon*, which is a three-dimensional block of uniform type.

There are many different classifications of soil and this makes the simple discussion of soil types difficult. In this book, the main processes of soil development will be discussed and where more than one name for a soil type exists, the alternative names are also given. In some cases, for example where new and old classifications exist, it is not necessarily easy to equate the name of one soil type with another; this problem is examined further in Chapter seven.

Inputs and outputs

If we look back at Figure 2 (p. 3) we can see that several soil inputs and outputs are given. We can now use the systems analysis concept of inputs and outputs (introduced in section 1.1) to help in understanding the formation of differing soil types. The three most important inputs and outputs are:

1 *The input and output of parent material* – this

controls the depth of the soil B horizon.

2 *The input and output of humus* – this controls A horizon thickness.

3 *The input and output of water* – this controls the solution and leaching processes and also indirectly the accumulation of organic matter.

In many ways the input and output of water is the most important factor, and as the amount of water passing downwards through a soil increases, the amount of solutes moved by leaching also increases. If the water inputs are very large then surface wetness tends to occur. This inhibits the oxidation of organic matter and raw, acid, mor humus will accumulate. As organic matter accumulates, the solution of minerals by cheluviation tends to increase (Figure 38). In hotter climates where evaporation exceeds precipitation, water tends to pass upwards to the soil surface, especially during a dry season following a wet season. This upward movement offsets leaching, often giving rise to the accumulation of salts at the surface. Soils forming where evaporation exceeds precipitation are considered on p. 41.

Now, if we examine the mineral situation, we see that, as the input of weathered material increases, soil depth also increases. But if the output of weathered material is greater than the input then soil erosion must be occurring and soil depth decreases. This happens on steep slopes and also in some unvegetated areas.

Parent material and soil depth

In some cases soil development may be limited by the lack of weathered parent material. This is the case over very hard rocks, which weather only examples are over glacial tills, clays, sands, gravels,

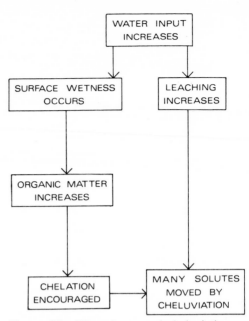

Figure 38 Water input and cheluviation

slowly and do not yield any depth of granular material (such as basalt, well-cemented sandstone and Carboniferous (Mississippian) Limestone). Thus the soil depth is limited by the lack of mineral input.

Where a thick deposit of parent material occurs soil formation is not limited by this factor and alluvium, colluvium (slope foot deposits), loess and head (periglacial deposits). Thus, in Figure 39, we can describe two main situations, one where the depth of soil formation is limited by mineral material input (I) and one where it is not (II). A further subdivision (I_1) is necessary where soil formation is limited by a large output and (I_2) where formation is limited by a small input.

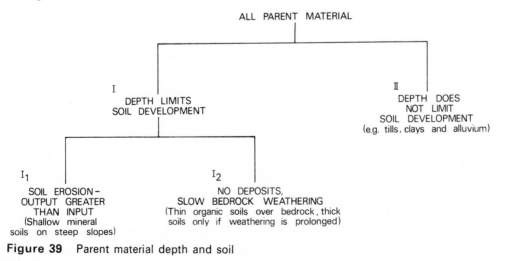

Figure 39 Parent material depth and soil

Soil development on deeper parent materials

We can now look at the deeper soils where the input supply of mineral matter is not a limiting factor. To understand soil development and horizonation attention will have to be paid to the other soil inputs and outputs – soil humus and soil water.

It was shown in section 1.1 that soil developed when a parent material reacted when tending to achieve a state of equilibrium with its environmental conditions. Where precipitation exceeds evaporation, three main cases of differing environmental conditions concerning water are important and they rely on the balance of (a) rainfall input, and (b) drainage water output:

1 where water outputs are equal to water inputs (drainage is good) but the inputs are small (yearly rainfall is not heavy),
2 where outputs are equal to inputs but the inputs are large (high rainfall), and
3 where the rate of output does not keep pace with the rate of input (drainage is poor); rainfall input high or low.

Four soil development processes arise from these three cases – leaching, clay translocation, podzolization and gleying:

leaching is the downwashing of soluble material;
clay translocation is the downwashing of clays; this is also termed *lessivage* (pronounced to rhyme with 'massage');
podzolization is the downwashing of most of the soil solutes by cheluviation, leaving a bleached white or grey upper soil mineral horizon;
gleying is the term given to the soil-forming processes occurring in waterlogged soils where alternate oxidizing and reducing conditions are present according to the level of water in the soil.

We can now look at these four soil development processes in connection with the three environmental cases of water balance described above.

Leaching, clay translocation and podzolization occur where the drainage is good. The differences between the three are that they represent an increase in movement of water down the soil profile due to increasing amounts of rainfall input. However, a crucial step is that as surface wetness increases organic matter accumulation also increases. Thus cheluviation increases as rainfall input increases. Therefore during the podzolization process the accumulation of a thick mat of humus on top of the soil occurs and many more nutrients and clays are washed down the soil profile than in simple leaching (see Figures 8 and 44).

We can see that the simple term leaching is inadequate to describe the overall soil development processes which also involve the movement of clays and chelates. The term leaching is usually reserved for the movement of solutes in waters. The general term of *Eluviation* is used for overall washing out or removal of any material and the term *Illuviation* for washing in to the lower horizons. These terms are similar, but if the analogy with *ex*it is used for *el*uviation and *in* for *ill*uviation they should be easier to remember. Eluvial horizons are termed E horizons (see p. 92).

Soil types where precipitation exceeds evaporation

This section describes soil development simply with respect to rainfall and other factors. Soil classification is described in further detail in Chapter 7. The different types of soil development processes described above are reflected in horizon variations

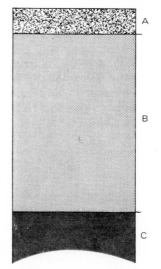

Figure 40 Acid brown earth

and hence in soil type. In temperate climates the sequence of soil changes in response to increasing rainfall input (but with good drainage conditions maintained) is as follows:

1 low to moderate rainfall input: *acid brown earth*;
2 moderate rainfall input: *brown earth* (*sol lessivé*);
3 moderate to high input: *podzolic brown earth*;
4 high rainfall input: *podzol*. (USDA system, spodosol, subsurface accumulations of iron, aluminium and organic matter).

1 ACID BROWN EARTH
The A horizon is capped by a mull or moder humus.

35

The B horizon shows little signs of differentiation except that it may be slightly lighter coloured in the upper horizons due to the removal of solutes. A typical profile is described in Figure 40. No clay and very little iron has been washed down the profile. Only the most soluble elements, like calcium and magnesium, are being actively removed. The pH will be on the acid side, about pH 5, ranging possibly from pH 4·5 to pH 6·5.

2 BROWN EARTH (SOL LESSIVÉ)
The distinctive characteristic of this soil is that clay has been translocated down through the soil profile. The lower B horizon is rich in clay and therefore can be distinguished from the rest of the profile by its texture. This is termed a textural B horizon or a Bt horizon (Figure 41). Some iron is also moved

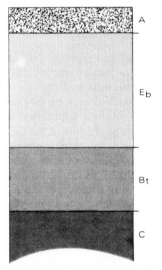

Figure 41 Brown earth (sol lessivé)

down the profile. It is thought that the clay is washed down the profile in a jelly-like solution and that the clay is deposited in a skin or *cutan*, which can be seen in thin section (see section 2.5), lower down the profile (Figure 42).

3 PODZOLIC BROWN EARTH
This soil is transitional between a brown earth and a podzol. Not only will some of the more soluble elements and clays have been washed down, but also cheluviation is becoming dominant. Thus a fairly thick accumulation of acid organic matter is present at the surface, and if the mineral horizon immediately under the organic matter is carefully examined some bleached, pale coloured sand grains can be seen. This is because much of the iron, which gives the soils a reddish colour when oxidized, is

36

being actively removed in chelates. Furthermore, as well as the light coloured grains in the upper soil, some darker colouring may be visible in the lower profile. This is the redeposition of iron and possibly some of the organic matter that acted as a chelatory carrier. A B horizon rich in iron is termed a Bfe horizon and one rich in downwashed humus a Bh horizon (Figure 43).

4 PODZOL
A podzol can be recognised by the presence of an upper dark organic matter horizon and a paler eluvial horizon beneath (Figure 44). The upper A horizon is very dark brown or black and is composed of acid, mor humus. Below this is a grey or white bleached horizon of pale coloured mineral grains, often of quartz. Much of the iron has been lost from this horizon. Below this layer darker horizons occur. These may have downwashed humus present or downwashed iron or both. The horizon thus may be dark with humus or reddish with iron, or a mixture of both. In fact, the iron is often moved down in combination with organic matter in the form of chelates (see p. 7). The movement and reprecipitation of iron down a soil profile is a complex process which may involve organic matter, as suggested above, and the reduction and oxidation of iron. The reasons for the precipitation of iron may also involve changes in pH, iron tending to be precipitated in solutions which become less acid. In addition, the presence of iron may reduce the solubility of organic compounds, leading to their precipitation. Thus, below a distinct leached horizon, which is the most diagnostic feature of a podzol, there may be an iron rich horizon with a greater or lesser degree of distinctness, ranging from a diffuse reddish layer to a prominent iron pan.

Podzols may therefore be subdivided into a variety of types such as iron pan podzols or humus-iron podzols according to the development of this layer. A well developed podzol profile is best seen on porous, acid parent material, such as a quartz sand, in areas of high rainfall and where there is good drainage. Such a profile is illustrated in Figure 44, showing a prominent bleached eluvial horizon, an Ea horizon (E = eluvial, a = ash like or albic, that is white or pale coloured) and a lower iron rich horizon, a Bfe horizon.

Gleying

Where soil water output is not rapid the soil is liable to *gleying*. If water stays in a soil for a long time the soil pores remain filled with water. This does

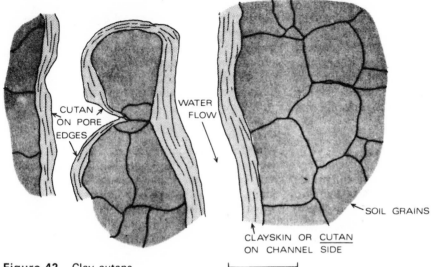

CUTAN ON PORE EDGES

WATER FLOW

SOIL GRAINS

CLAYSKIN OR <u>CUTAN</u> ON CHANNEL SIDE

Figure 42 Clay cutans

1mm

not mean that all oxygen is immediately excluded as some can be dissolved in the water (this is how fishes and other aquatic life respire). But the oxygen in the soil water will be quickly used up by the soil microorganisms. Gaseous diffusion is slower in water than it is in air and thus water which is stagnant in a soil soon becomes deoxygenated and the oxygen is not quickly replaced by diffusion from the surface. The iron in the soil becomes reduced because of the lack of oxygen and this gives the soil a greenish or bluish tinge, which is the characteristic background colour of a gley soil (see section 1.2).

However, the most distinctive feature of a gley soil is a scattering of red mottles. These are places where fresh oxygenated water or air have been able to penetrate and oxidize the iron. Thus the larger soil pores, structural cracks and root channels are red with precipitates of oxidized iron. The upper parts of the profile tend to be redder or browner and the lower parts paler greeny-blue. This is because the position of the water table will fluctuate in the soil according to season and the lower parts will be more permanently waterlogged than the upper.

All soil types may show signs of gleying and thus a gleyed brown earth or a gleyed podzol are possible.

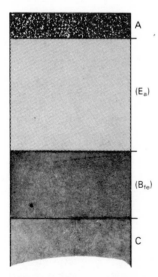

A

(E_a)

(B_{fe})

C

Figure 43 Podzolic brown earth
(brackets indicate weak development of horizon)

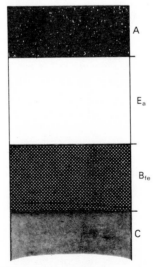

A

E_a

B_{fe}

C

Figure 44 Podzol
(B_{fe} may be weakly or strongly developed, E_a horizon is most diagnostic feature)

37

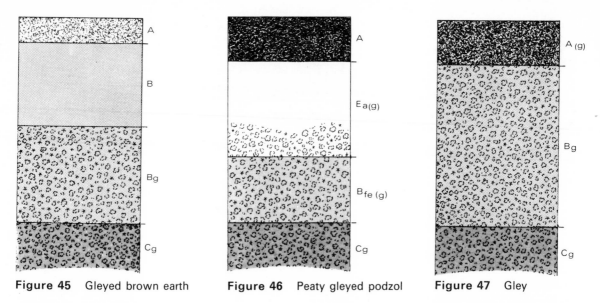

Figure 45   Gleyed brown earth   **Figure 46**   Peaty gleyed podzol   **Figure 47**   Gley

GLEYED BROWN EARTH

The overall appearance is of an acid brown earth, with little movement of clays or solutes, but the B horizon is mottled (Figure 45).

PEATY GLEYED PODZOL

This is a common soil in temperate upland areas where rainfall is high. High rainfall means two things – that leaching is encouraged and that gleying is encouraged. Thus, a podzol may be formed by leaching, but very high rainfall, especially in winter, may lead to the mottling of some of the soil horizons. A peaty gleyed podzol may show mottling below the iron pan, and in some places the iron pan may become so well developed as to be impermeable to water. Mottling may then occur above the iron pan. Podzols with gleying are usually accompanied by the accumulation of a very thick peaty A horizon and they are often referred to as *peaty gleyed podzols* (Figure 46), whereas the simpler podzols without gleying may be referred to as *humus-iron podzols*.

GLEYS

True gleys are usually found in thick clay deposits and the lower profile is simply the unweathered clay. The upper horizons are mottled and merge into the organic horizons (Figure 47).

CALCAREOUS SOILS

Calcareous soils are those little affected by rainfall and leaching processes and owe their presence to a limestone parent material in areas of low rainfall. They can be developed *in situ* where the calcareous parent material breaks up and is distributed

38

throughout the soil profile or they can be developed in low-lying areas where calcium carbonate is washed in from surrounding limestone areas. In the latter case a gleyed calcareous soil may develop.

Calcareous soils do not occur on limestone when the rock does not break up easily and where rainfall is high. The calcium is easily leached out of the soil in these cases and is not readily replenished by weathering input from the base of the soil. Figure 48 shows the formation of calcareous and non-calcareous soils on calcareous bedrock according to the nature of the rock and the amount of rainfall. The *calcareous brown earth* and its horizons are shown in Figure 49.

Summary – water balance and soil type

The development of soil types on deep parent material is summarized in Figure 50. The progression from an acid brown earth to podzol as rainfall input increases is shown and the influence of a low drainage output is shown as causing gleying and peat growth.

The general distribution of soil types in relation to rainfall is shown in Figure 51, with increasing leaching and podzolization as wetness increases and with peat accumulation in very wet areas, as suggested by Figure 38 (p. 34).

Soils developed where mineral input is limited

These soils are generally much thinner than the ones described above and soil development is usually limited to the accumulation of organic matter. Some mineral matter is usually present, but this is incorporated into the organic matter. These soils

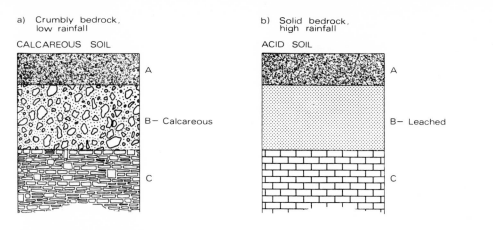

a) Crumbly bedrock, low rainfall

CALCAREOUS SOIL

- A
- B— Calcareous
- C

b) Solid bedrock, high rainfall

ACID SOIL

- A
- B— Leached
- C

Figure 48 Limestone soils

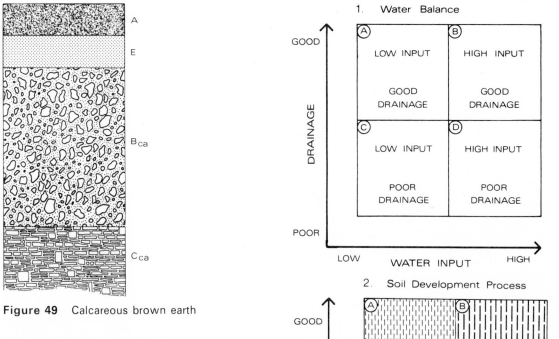

- A
- E
- B$_{ca}$
- C$_{ca}$

Figure 49 Calcareous brown earth

do not possess a mineral B horizon. A mixed mineral–organic A horizon overlays the hard rock C horizon. On hard limestone a *rendzina* soil occurs and on hard acid rocks a *ranker* occurs.

RENDZINA (Figure 52)
The humus is of the mull type and passes into limestone bedrock below.

RANKER (Figure 53)
The humus is of the mor type and passes into hard rock such as basalt or siliceous sandstone. The humus is usually wetter and more acid than in a rendzina.

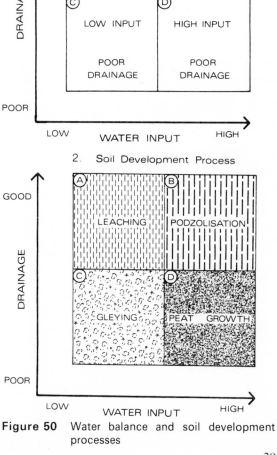

1. Water Balance

GOOD

(A)	(B)
LOW INPUT	HIGH INPUT
GOOD DRAINAGE	GOOD DRAINAGE
(C)	(D)
LOW INPUT	HIGH INPUT
POOR DRAINAGE	POOR DRAINAGE

DRAINAGE

POOR

LOW   WATER INPUT   HIGH

2. Soil Development Process

GOOD

(A) LEACHING (B) PODZOLISATION
(C) GLEYING (D) PEAT GROWTH

DRAINAGE

POOR

LOW   WATER INPUT   HIGH

Figure 50 Water balance and soil development processes

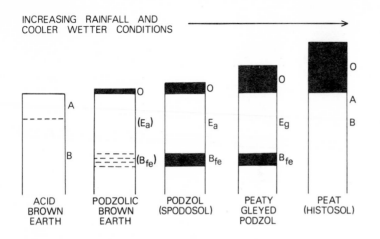

Figure 51 The relationship between increasing rainfall and soil types. Names in brackets are USDA terms for approximately the same soils

FIGURE RENDZINA   FIGURE RANKER

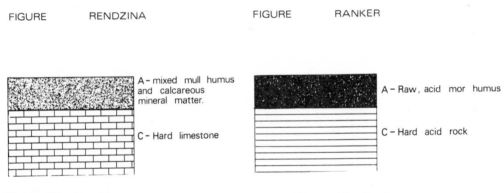

Figure 52 Rendzina   **Figure 53** Ranker

Deeply weathered tropical soils

Deeply weathered soils commonly occur on very old land surfaces in tropical regions. In many cases, soil development may have started in the Tertiary era, over 2-3 million years ago. Weathering has thus progressed to such an extent that many of the plant nutrients have been washed out of the soil, leaving residual clays, especially kaolinite, and iron and aluminium oxides together with resistant minerals, especially quartz. These constituents represent some of the simplest end products of weathering. Such soils occur under hot, moist conditions where weathering is intense and they commonly underlie tropical forest regions such as those of central South America and Africa. They are also found in grassland areas around tropical rain forests and other areas which are drier than the rain forest but where weathering and leaching have been prolonged, partly under

40

formerly wetter climatic regimes. In temperate regions glaciations caused considerable movement of soil parent material and many of the soil resources in these areas exist because of glacial action, as discussed further in Section 3.2. However, in equatorial regions and the surrounding areas which are now dry, parallel climatic modifications occurred during the period of glacial advances further north. In particular, there appears to have been a more extensive wetter zone than at present, covering areas which are now drier than the equatorial regions. This is true of much of the savanna grassland zones of South America and Africa and also in parts of Australia where deeply weathered soils occur. The most important factor in deep weathering is that the land surfaces on which the soils have developed have been in existence for long periods of time, without major reworking such as has occurred in northern glaciated areas.

One of the distinctive features of these soils is their red colouration. This is derived from the presence of residual insoluble iron oxides, as discussed on p. 7. The USDA classification for such soils uses the term *oxisols* to include many of these soils, the name conveying the importance of oxides in the soils many of which may have hard iron concretions present, termed *plinthite*. Other names include the terms *ferruginous* soils and *ferralitic soils*, both terms indicating the importance of iron. The term ferruginous soils is applied to soils in drier savanna areas and other areas around tropical rain forests. The term ferralitic soil is often given to the moister, more leached soils under tropical rain forest. Iron dominated, red soils are also often referred to as laterite (pronounced "latterite"). The term laterite is based on the Latin word *later* (pronounced "laater") which means brick: residual iron, clay soils may be formed into bricks which harden in the sun and air. As not all residual iron soils in the tropics exhibit this behaviour however, the more general term *latosol* is often used, with subdivisions of ferruginous and ferralitic soil (see Figure 54) or, increasingly the USDA term oxisol is used. A further soil type common in tropical areas is the *utisol*, again a deeply weathered soil, low in nutrient content but found in moist conditions and with a subsurface horizon of clay accumulation. Soils with a similar clay accumulation but which are less leached (i.e. in drier climates than oxisols or

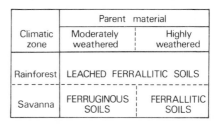

Climatic zone	Parent material	
	Moderately weathered	Highly weathered
Rainforest	LEACHED FERRALLITIC SOILS	
Savanna	FERRUGINOUS SOILS	FERRALLITIC SOILS

Figure 54   Residual iron soils, weathering and climate

utisols) are termed *alfisols* in the USDA system. The probable distribution of oxisols and utisols in central South America and Africa are shown in Figure 55, together with the less leached alfisols. The residual iron soils vary in their profile characteristics. In some cases, these soils are a deep uniform red colour where oxidation occurs throughout the profile, in others, insoluble oxidised iron is to be found in the upper layers while leaching of silicates has progressed beneath. In these cases there is a paler lower layer below, where simple clays, such as kaolinite, are present. The general process is illustrated in Figure 56 and examples of profiles are considered in section 3.4.

Soils where evaporation exceeds precipitation

In areas where evaporation exceeds precipitation, water tends to move upwards in the soil profile, at

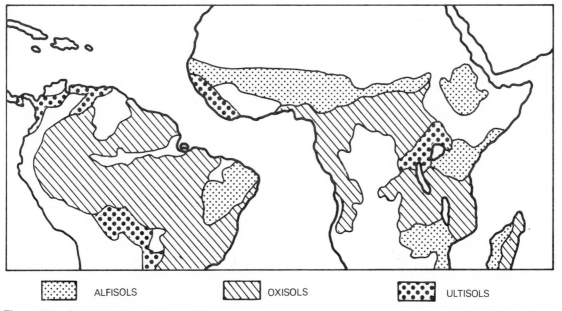

ALFISOLS   OXISOLS   ULTISOLS

Figure 55   Probable distribution of deeply weathered soils in Central South America and Africa (for explanation of terms see text above)

41

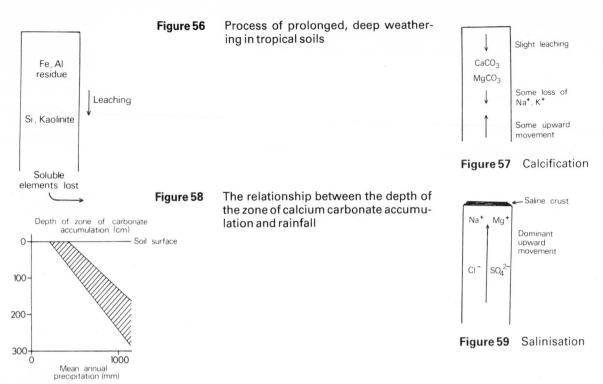

Figure 56 Process of prolonged, deep weathering in tropical soils

Fe, Al residue

Leaching

Si, Kaolinite

Soluble elements lost

Figure 57 Calcification

Slight leaching

CaCO₃
MgCO₃

Some loss of Na⁺, K⁺

Some upward movement

Figure 58 The relationship between the depth of the zone of calcium carbonate accumulation and rainfall

Depth of zone of carbonate accumulation (cm)

Soil surface

Mean annual precipitation (mm)

Figure 59 Salinisation

Saline crust

Na⁺ Mg⁺

Dominant upward movement

Cl⁻ SO₄²⁻

least seasonally. In some cases, rainfall moves downwards through the soil in the wet season but the direction is reversed during the dry season, with a net movement in the upwards direction. In other areas the water moving upwards may be derived from groundwater sources which are not immediately dependent on rainfall and so the upward movement may be more prolonged. The upward movement results in the accumulation of salts at the soil surface as the water evaporates. The balance between evaporation and precipitation may vary and the amount and types of salts accumulating will also vary. With a high evaporation to precipitation ratio most salts will be drawn to the surface but where evaporation and precipitation are more nearly balanced some of the highly soluble salts may be leached below the surface by seasonal rains, leaving the less soluble salts at the surface. With a close evaporation to precipitation ratio the highly soluble elements such as sodium and potassium tend to be leached to the subsoil with the less soluble elements calcium and magnesium left at the surface. This process is referred to as *calcification* (Figure 57) and is common in the continental interiors of Eurasia and North America. The depth of soil calcium carbonate accumulation is closely related to annual rainfall (Figure 58). Moving towards the equator, the higher ratio of evaporation over rainfall means that even the most sol-

uble salts will remain in the soil profile. This process is further encouraged in lowland situations where water, with dissolved chemical elements in it, collects from surrounding higher ground or where a groundwater supply of water exists near the surface. As the water rises to the surface, leaving the salts behind during evaporation, considerable amounts of salts accumulate at the surface. This process is termed *salinisation*. Sodium, magnesium, chloride and sulphate commonly accumulate at the surface as the salts sodium chloride and magnesium sulphate (Figure 59). Note that not only common salt, sodium chloride, is involved but also other salts (given that the chemical definition of a salt is a substance that dissociates in water to yield both a cation and an anion, excluding those with yield H^+ cations, which are acids).

Saline soils do not occupy large proportions of the earth's surface but their importance lies in the fact that where they do occur they often represent the only potentially cultivable land in otherwise arid areas. The understanding and management of saline soils are thus important topics which are discussed further in Chapter five. Saline soils may be given the term *solonchak* which are those simply dominated by the presence of free salts. A further type is often recognised where there is an extremely high sodium content adsorbed onto the clay surfaces. Here the term *solenetz* is used and these soils have a highly dispersed soil structure and low permeability.

3.2   The time factor in soil development

The legacy of the Pleistocene

Between about 1–2 million years ago and 10 000 years ago many areas which are now temperate were covered with a series of ice sheets. These acted to clear away any pre-existing soil and other weathered material from highland areas and to deposit this in lowland areas. Thus in high mountain areas the post-glacial soil parent material was bare rock. In valleys and lowland plains glacial till, together with sands and gravel, form soil parent materials (Figure 60). The numerous effects of the Pleistocene ice sheets can be seen in the materials which have been left available as soil parent materials:

1 the glacially scoured rock in uplands
2 the deposits of boulder clay or till in the lower lands;
3 the deposits of windblown deposits, notably loess and sand dunes;

4 the deposits of fluvio-glacial sands and gravels;
5 the periglacial head deposits (such as coombe rock), frost wedges and colluvium (slope-foot deposits);
6 river alluvium that has accumulated from the Pleistocene to the present day (previous deposits often having been covered or eroded);
7 peat deposits that have accumulated in the wettest times since the Pleistocene.

The significance to soil development of glacial processes is that, wherever deep mineral soils are found in temperate areas, with the exception of river alluvium, they are often the result of glacial deposition (boulder clay and loess), coupled with slope-washing and slope-creep processes of periglacial times.

Loess is recognised as an important constituent of soil in areas around ice sheets. Not all sizes of mineral grains can be readily blown by the wind. The largest particles are too heavy but the smallest are light enough to have been blown considerable distances. Loess deposits are therefore made up of intermediate size ranges, that is of silt size. Deep deposits of silt-sized material can therefore be found in areas adjacent to glacial ice sheets, de-

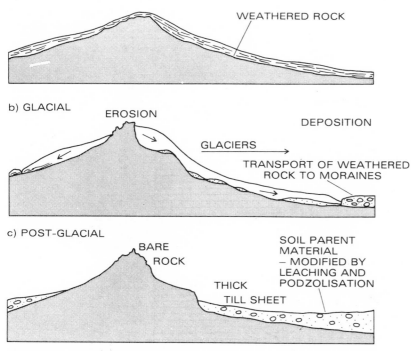

Figure 60   Glaciation and soil parent material

43

rived by wind action or unvegetated glacial moraine and outwash material. As well as the deeper deposits, thinner bands are present in many soils, for example in southern Britain, where, however, they are less obvious and care is needed to distinguish the presence of loess from translocated material derived from higher up in the soil profile. The contribution of loess to soils is becoming widely recognised in southern Britain (Figure 61) and much of Europe outside the more well known thicker deposits of north Germany and also China where deposits several metres thick

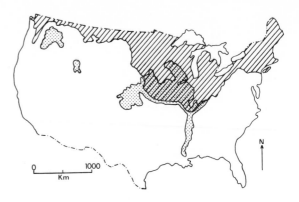

 Glacial till
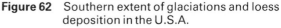 Loess

Figure 62 Southern extent of glaciations and loess deposition in the U.S.A.

occur. The contribution of the Pleistocene glaciations to soil development in the USA is shown in Figure 62.

Peat formation in many upland temperate areas dates from about mid-post-glacial times when a wet, cool period of climate (referred to as the Atlantic Period) occurred. Before this time podzolization was taking place and it is common in upland areas to find soil profiles with an old soil or *palaeosol* buried beneath a thick layer of peat. The tree roots of the former vegetation may often still be seen in the growth position in the buried soil layer (Figure 63).

Soil development in tropical areas has not been interrupted as it has been in glacial areas, but there have been substantial modifications to the soil environment during the history of these areas, notably, because of wetter regimes during the Tertiary

A = Covered in all glaciations.
B = Covered in ice, but not in the last glacial; loess and periglacial features present.
C = Not covered by ice; loess and periglacial features.

Figure 61 Southern extent of glaciations and loess deposition in Britain

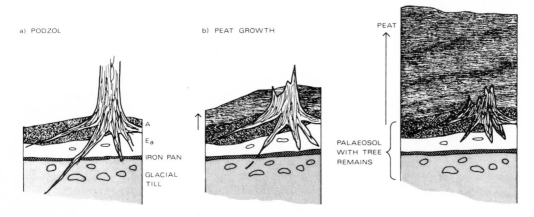

Figure 63 Palaeosol under peat

44

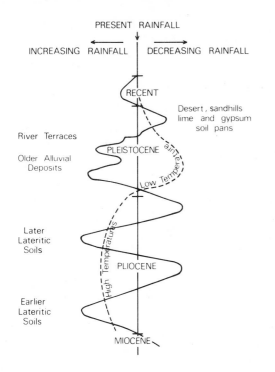

Figure 64 Climate changes and soil development in Australia

and Pleistocene. In Australia, the relationship of climatic change and soil formation is shown in Figure 64. Some of the initial development of the earlier oxidised iron rich soils is thought to have originated during the Miocene and Pliocene.

The rate of soil change

Can one soil type change into another, and if so how long does it take? Does an acid brown earth change into a podzol given enough time and enough rainfall? It is very difficult to answer these questions, as observations on soils have only been made over the last century or so.

However, some evidence concerning the slow rate of soil development comes from studies of river alluvium. In the most recent river deposits horizonation is virtually nonexistent, yet in the older deposits of alluvium (such as those left on river terraces), signs of horizonation can be seen. The most soluble material is being leached from the surface layers of the soil and it is very likely that, given enough time, the constituents of the soil will be redistributed throughout the profile in accordance with the equilibrium theory discussed earlier (Chapter one). The extent of the redistribution will depend upon the rainfall and the drainage conditions.

The evaluation of the rate of soil change is an important problem. Realizing that soil develops in adaptation to environmental conditions it should be noted that the environmental conditions have usually been modified by man. For example, much natural vegetation has been changed by man and soils have long been cultivated by man. Soils originally under woodland may have been changed greatly by cultivation. Structure and nutrient status are perhaps most easily changed by cultivation, while texture is conversely probably the most difficult characteristic to change. Man is changing the soil-developing environment – how far and how rapidly will the soil change in response to cultivation?

Certain soil horizons have been recognized as being virtually manmade. An Ap horizon, for example, is one where the structures are changed by ploughing. In America phosphate-rich horizons are recognized. These have developed from a long history of fertilizer application. Clearly structure and nutrient status have been changed in a few hundred years of cultivation.

Soil development is not a process that proceeds to a certain stage and then stops. It is in many ways a continuing process. The weathering of parent material proceeds continually – the components of the soil continually adjusting to each other and to external factors such as climate. While some soil components, like resistant quartz grains, may have survived unchanged since glacial times, other components, especially the soil plasma with its secondary minerals and soil structures and horizons may have changed many times since glacial times in response to changing environmental conditions. Man is now one of the more dominant forces manipulating soil for his own use for the production of food: soil management is the topic for Chapter five.

3.3   Soil on slopes

Just as soil changes over time, it also changes over space. As most of the earth's surface is not flat it is important to understand how slope affects the variations of soil over space.

Slope has two principal effects on soil development. It affects drainage and soil stability.

Drainage

Water will obviously drain more quickly on a steep slope than it will on a less steep slope. Thus flatter areas tend to be waterlogged and here peat grows and gleying takes place. Soils on slope crests tend to be more leached and the nutrients washed from the upper slope pass to the lower slopes, which are

45

consequently richer in nutrients.

It is clear that it is necessary to work out the direction and ease of flow of water movement on a slope before soil development can be fully understood.

It is clear that it is necessary to work out the direction and ease of flow of water movement on a slope before soil development can be fully understood. Water leaches nutrients from the soil and transports them through the soil and also through the bedrock if it is permeable. In the case of the less permeable bedrocks, plateaus tend to be wetter while slope crests and the slopes themselves are

linked soil types. While each soil on the slope is recognizable as separate, each is linked to the next in terms of its relative position. (See Appendix 4).

Catenas have long been recognised in African soils where the sequences shown in Figure 66 are common. The more iron rich, oxidised soils, often with plinthite occur on the slope tops, with wetter soils below. In other areas, less weathered rock masses occur towards the tops of slopes with more weathered soils on the slopes. Erosion and deposition may also influence sequences of soil changes on slopes, as described below.

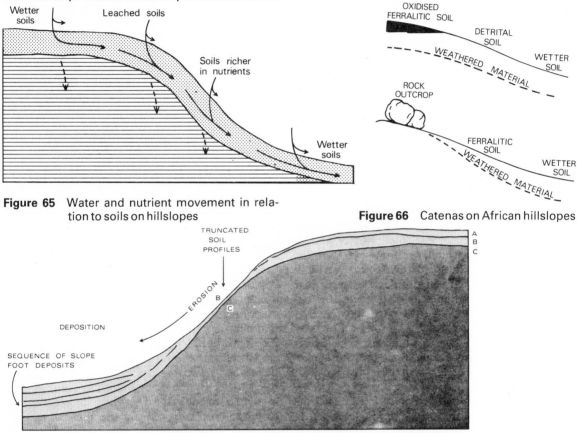

Figure 65 Water and nutrient movement in relation to soils on hillslopes

Figure 66 Catenas on African hillslopes

Figure 67 Soil truncation on slopes

well drained, passing their water downslope to the slope foot. Thus, the upper soils on a slope tend to be leached while wetter, more nutrient rich soils occur at slope foot sites, (Figure 65). This process is less marked on permeable bedrocks.

Sequences of soil changes down slopes, such as those in Figure 65 are termed *catenas* when they are developed regularly in similar topographic positions. The word catena comes from the Latin for a chain; thus the concept implies a series of

46

Soil stability

Soils on flat areas will be stable but on steep slopes they will begin to slide downhill under the influence of gravity. Soil creep and slope wash are also active on steep slopes and these combined actions lead to a thinning of soils on slopes. Soil profiles can appear 'cut short' or *truncated* when compared with surrounding stable areas. Figure 67 shows fully developed soil profiles at the crest of the hill but erosion of the soil on the slope leads to truncation of the profile. Downslope the eroded material is redeposited as layers and sometimes buried soils can be detected at the bottom of slopes. These have been formed and then buried by deposits from above.

Summary

The factors of slope drainage and slope stability account for soil differences on a slope. In stable areas the direction of water movement influences the course of soil development (soil water is discussed further in section 4.2). In unstable areas on steep slopes the course of soil development is limited by the depth of soil that can accumulate, in other words by the balance of inputs and outputs of soil materials.

The catenary concept is a useful one in the understanding of the evolution of soil on slopes. Once the basic pattern has been identified a detailed picture of soil on slopes can be quickly established, using the idea that each soil type up or down the slope may be linked in a soil catena.

3.4   Case studies of soil development

In this section, selected soil profiles will be examined, with an attempt to understand the development of the soil in each particular example. Both field description and also laboratory analysis may be involved in the interpretation of a soil profile and the discussion of its origin and classification.

Case study 1· Podzol (USDA Spodosol)

Depth from surface (cm)	Horizon	Horizon description
0–2	L	Undecomposed litter
2–4	F	Partially decomposed litter
4–7	H	Well-decomposed humus, low in mineral content
7–20	Ea	Eluvial horizon, bleached and ash-like
20–30	Bfe	Illuvial horizon, rich in iron
30–35	B/C	Horizon of weathering bedrock, transitional between B horizon above and C horizon below
35 +	C	Little altered bedrock, a mica schist

DEVELOPMENT

In this profile analyses show that organic matter

and iron have been washed through the Ea horizon and deposited in the Bfe horizon. In the B/C horizon of the profile the rock is weathered. Mica is decomposed and clay (probably illite) is formed. Quartz, which is relatively insoluble, remains fairly constant through the profile and is almost untouched by soil development processes. Mica, on the other hand, may be attacked by hydrolysis and decreases in quantity up the profile.

In this case mineral, chemical and textural analyses reveal a twofold story of bedrock weathering: the selective decomposition of easily weathered minerals in the bedrock and the movement of iron and humus down the profile by eluviation.

Case study 2 · Brown earth

Depth from surface (cm)	Horizon	Horizon description
0–20	Ap	Mixed mineral-organic layer (A) homogenised by ploughing (p), humose silt loam
20–45	Eb	Pale brown (b) eluvial (E) horizon, silt loam
45–60	Bt	Silty clay, B horizon distinguished by its textural change (t)
60+	C	Bedrock

This is a brown earth soil with little marked development except for a slight leaching in the upper mineral horizon and a slight accumulation in the lower horizon. The surface has been homogenised by ploughing, giving rise to an Ap horizon. Below this there has been loss of soluble material, giving a pale horizon, an eluvial E horizon, but this is darker than the Ea horizon described in case study 1 above; the brown colour gives it an Eb notation. Below this is a Bt horizon, which is a B horizon distinguished by its textural change, in this case an increase in the proportion of finer material. This will reflect the presence of downwashed clay or, alternatively it could reflect the contribution of wind blown loess to the soil profile (as discussed on p. 44). Detailed examination of a thin section of the soil using a microscope (see p.18) will reveal whether or not clay skins or cutans are present as characteristic evidence of clay movement down through a soil (see p.36 and 37). In addition, mineralogical evidence could detect the presence of foreign windblown minerals derived from loess and not present in the bedrock (see p.44).

Case study 3 · Ferruginous soil (USDA: oxisol)

Depth from surface (cm)	Horizon	Horizon description
0–20	Ap	Mixed mineral organic layer (A), homogenised by ploughing (p) Dark reddish brown, sandy clay
20–70	Bt	B Horizon distinguished by textural change (t). Reddish brown, clay (small amount of sand)
70+	B2	Second B horizon. Dark red, sand clay, weak structures

In this case the soil has again been homogenised by cultivation in the upper layers so that the organic matter is incorporated into the Ap layer, giving it a brown colour. The Bt horizon contains some clay translocated from above, giving a blocky structure. Below this is a soil which contains few weatherable minerals and which is very friable (crumbly to the touch). A distinctive feature is the red colouration throughout, associated with prolonged weathering and the oxidation of iron compounds.

Cast study 4 · Solonetz

Depth from surface (cm)	Horizon	Horizon description
0–15	A	Mixed mineral-organic layer thin, sandy horizon
15–40	Bt	B Horizon distinguished by texture (t). Dense grey, clay horizon, rounded columnar structures, high in sodium.
40+	Bg	Mottled gleyed (g) clay B horizon

Here, the topsoil has been depleted of clay while the subsoil is dominated by clay. The high sodium content has acted to disperse the clay but massive columnar structures have developed with rounded tops, the soil is compact and very dense; the topsoil often lacks structure. The lower part of the profile frequently shows signs of impeded drainage, with mottling.

Case study 5 · gleyed brown earth/sol lessivé on chalk

This is a complex soil profile. It is included to demonstrate what steps may be involved in the understanding of some deeper soils with a long history of varied development.

Depth from surface (cm)	Horizon	Horizon description
0–2	L	Undecomposed litter
2–4	F	Partially decomposed litter
4–15	A	Humose loam
15–30	Eb	Loam, eluvial
30–40	Bt	Clay, illuvial
40–60	Bg	Gleyed clay loam
60–70	CI	Clay loam with flints
70+	CII	Chalk

DEVELOPMENT

Both soil development processes and past geomorphological processes have to be investigated in order to understand this profile. There are two parent material horizons, CI and CII. The CI horizon is a clay deposit with flints (derived from chalk) and is thought to have been derived by Tertiary weathering processes. This separates the chalk (CII) from the rest of the soil profile. For this reason, while the chalk itself is calcareous and porous the soil is in fact acid and poorly drained, deriving its character from the clay deposit rather than from the chalk. Thus the lower layers of the soil are gleyed because water is held up on the relatively impermeable clay loam. Above this gleyed layer is a horizon where clay has been washed in and deposited from the overlying Eb horizon.

In summary, to understand the development of this complex soil profile it is necessary to include studies of the following:

1 the geomorphological history – the formation of clay with flints over chalk;
2 the gleying process – the perched water table on the clay, and
3 clay translocation – clay being washed down as far as the gleyed layer.

Case study 6 · calcareous brown earth with gleying

This soil profile is developed on glacial till.

Depth from surface (cm)	Horizon	Horizon description
0–20	Ap	Clay loam
20–60	Bg	Clay loam with gleying, slightly calcareous
60+	Cg	Clay loam with chalk, gleyed

DEVELOPMENT

In this profile the Ap horizon is a mixture of organic and mineral matter. The soil is developed from glacial till which was derived from a chalky area. Investigation of the till below the soil shows it to be composed of clay and chalk fragments. The high clay content means that the drainage is poor in the lower part of the profile and gleying occurs. However, the Bg horizon is gleyed and calcareous below, but towards the top drainage is better and some of the chalk has been leached from the top of the horizon. In the A horizon all the chalk has been leached out and the soil is acid.

Observations on gleying, analysis of calcium carbonate content and pH reveal the story of soil development. In the upper part of the profile, where drainage is adequate, leaching occurs and the chalk is absent. In the lower part of the profile water is stagnant more often. Leaching is not encouraged, the soil remains calcareous and gleying occurs.

While a chalky till shows these features particularly well because chalk is easily soluble in rain water, other glacial tills show the same type of picture of leaching at the surface. The materials deposited by glacial processes are being redistributed by the soil development processes, especially leaching.

Summary

It is often necessary to gather data of a diverse nature in order to attempt to fully understand the development of a soil profile. In the examples selected not only simple data, like texture, are required (for distinguishing Bt horizons, for example), but also more complex mineralogical, chemical or organic analysis may be needed, especially where the more detailed soil profiles, such as the gleyed brown earth/sol lessivé on chalk, are concerned.

Conclusions

Soils are often classified according to their visible characteristics in the field. Soil genesis can often also be inferred from soil pit inspection. In many cases, however, further laboratory analysis is necessary, involving soil mineralogy, chemistry and thin section study before the origin of a soil can be more fully understood.

4

Soils in the ecosystem

4.1 The ecosystem approach

Systems analysis

Applying systems analysis to soil study is useful because we are able to understand the development of soils by working out inputs and outputs, as explained in Section 1.1. A systems approach is characterized by examination of changes or movements – in this case *movement of materials*, like water and nutrients, from one location to another.

An important aspect of systems analysis is that we can look at small systems or sections of systems (*subsystems*) and combine these in larger systems. In this way we may be able to understand how something works by seeing that the output of one subsystem becomes the input of another system. For example, nutrients from the soil subsystem are taken up by the plant subsystem and a *nutrient output* or loss in terms of the soil becomes a *nutrient*

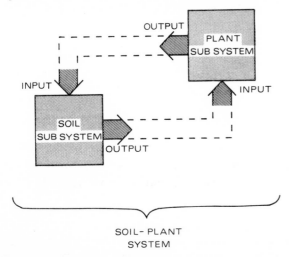

Figure 68   Linked subsystems

input or gain in the *plant* subsystem (Figure 68). We may consider the soil by itself as an isolated system and look at its internal functioning or we may look at the soil and plant systems and study their interactions. Furthermore, we may attempt to place soil in relation to all the factors that interact with it – to study soil in the ecosystem.

50

Although we may break down subjects like soil study and plant study into various components in order to be able to understand them, it is important to be able to put the components back again to see how the system works as a whole. An everyday analogy is when something goes wrong with a record player. It is necessary to understand how the internal parts work to mend it. It is not sufficient to be able to identify the individual components such as the needle or the turntable; we also need to know how these are all related in producing the sounds we hear from the overall system. Similarly with the soil–plant system. In this case the desired result is a useful crop. If we want to produce the best crop we must understand the individual parts of the system and how they react as a whole to produce the crop. Again, using the record-player analogy, many of us happily use the instrument without knowing anything about the detailed internal workings. We can identify the switch and the needle as the key components. We can make two statements:

1 It is not necessary to know all the details of a system all the time to manage the system in a satisfactory way.
2 It is only necessary to know the details if we want to correct something that has gone wrong with the system.

Obviously there are a multitude of complex factors which influence the overall behaviour of a system. We can divide components into two groups: first *principal operators*, which are the key features to know in order to work the system; and second the *secondary components*, which do not have a major influence on the system output but are important to the detailed working of the system.

Systems analysis uses three levels of detail of analysis:

1 *Black-box analysis* where only the principal inputs and outputs are studied.
2 *Grey-box analysis* where some detail of the internal workings is known.

3 *White-box analysis* where all the detailed components and controls on input and output are known.

In the soil–plant system several levels of analysis are appropriate. In some cases it is sufficient to see a wilting plant and to know that the input of water has been insufficient. The detailed mechanisms of water uptake are, as far as this problem is concerned, secondary and unimportant. Simple black-box analysis is appropriate: the solution is self-evident. In other cases a crop may develop a curious symptom of an unknown disease. In this case a more detailed analysis is necessary. It is necessary to look at soil conditions, pests in the soil, soil nutrients, soil water and a whole host of other inputs and outputs which may be affecting the plant.

While the above examples may have appeared obvious, in other cases it may not be so. It can be said that in essence systems analysis provides a means of solving problems by attempting to resolve inputs and outputs into principal (important) and secondary (less important) factors. The more complex a problem the more a white-box analysis may have to be used, though even complex problems can be 'short cut' by use of a few major factors which may solve the problem.

Ecosystems

One of the largest, most complex systems is the ecosystem. Soils, climate, plants, rocks and animals all interact in a multiplicity of ways. If we are to fully understand how our environment works it is not possible to look at one subject, that of soils, in isolation from the rest of the components in the ecosystem. Nature does not divide herself into neat compartments and therefore to understand her we must

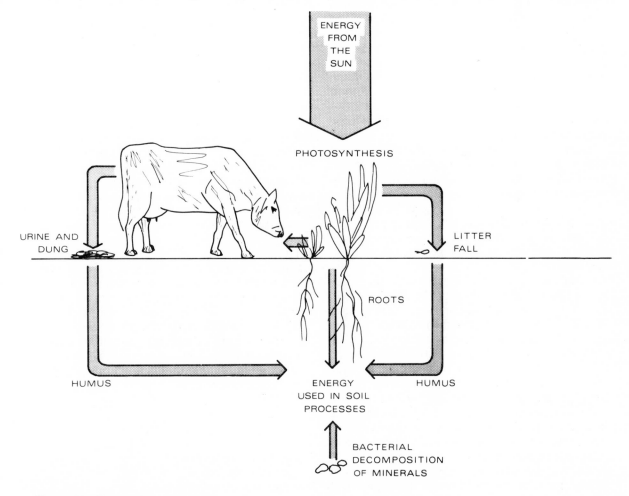

Figure 69 Energy flow into a soil

51

integrate our separate pieces of knowledge into an interacting whole. We shall study the ecosystem from the point of view of how the soil fits into the overall ecosystem. It will not be necessary to know everything about everything all of the time (even if it were possible!), but different levels of detail will be necessary to solve different problems.

ENERGY

The primary driving force of the ecosystem is the sun's energy. This is utilized in plants during photosynthesis. The energy thus stored may take several routes to become an input into the soil in order to become the driving force of soil processes.

To solve the problem of understanding how soil gets its energy we need to study the links between plants, animals and the soil and also between plants and the soil direct (Figure 69). When an animal eats a plant much of the energy is used in the animal's metabolism, but some remains in the animal's faeces and urine which is deposited on the soil. As far as the cow in Figure 69 is concerned it has finished with the organic matter and it is a system output. But as far as the soil is concerned this is a system input. Soil microorganisms readily obtain energy from the dung and are able to live by decomposing the material. That which remains is incorporated into the soil, where it provides a store for plant roots to tap.

The plant also sheds its leaves. (Even if the plant is evergreen, each leaf may only last for up to two years before it is shed: the plant appears evergreen because all the leaves are not shed at once.) Thus organic matter is continually being added as an output from the plant system but as an input to the soil system. Leaves again supply a source of energy that soil organisms can use for growth and metabolism.

Plant roots provide a kind of motivation force as they push their way through the soil. They help to form structures and they supply a link in the cycling of nutrients by cation exchange. When they die they add organic matter to the soil.

Within the soil a whole series of systems can be identified which are based on discarded organic matter from the plant and animal systems. Herbivorous organisms feed on plant remains and carnivorous organisms feed in turn on the herbivorous ones. Parasites also live on other organisms and on plant roots and so there is a closely linked web of interacting food chains.

The bacteria in the soil are primary operators in this system. They are the ultimate decomposers of all wastes left by other processes and other food chains. They can obtain energy and carbon from organic matter. This type of nutrition is termed *heterotrophic nutrition* (*hetero* – many sources: *trophic* – feeding). Many bacteria, fungi and actinomycetes and all animals feed in this way.

A source of energy for the soil not so far considered is that of minerals. We saw in an earlier section (2.9) how bacteria could decompose minerals. They in fact obtain energy and nutrition from this source. This is termed *chemo-autotrophic nutrition*. The term autotroph (*auto* – self; *troph* – feeding) implies that energy is gained by a primary source like the sun (in which case it is *photo-autotrophic nutrition*), or from the oxidation of inorganic compounds. Carbon is obtained from carbon dioxide. In the case of bacteria deriving energy from minerals the energy has been locked in the mineral for many thousands of years since the initial formation of the mineral in geological time.

Figure 70 shows a simplified food web for the soil. *Phytophages* feed on living plants, *saprophytes* feed on decayed matter and *microphytes* feed on bacteria, algae and fungal hyphae. *Carnivores* feed on soil animals. All organisms decay and provide organic matter. Some organisms can perform more than one function. In terms of systems we have looked at plant, animal and geological subsystems and also at the major ecosystem input – sunlight. We have understood the energy input into the soil subsystem by looking at the principal operators – the bacteria, the animals eating the plants and the plants photosynthesizing. It has not been necessary to look in great detail at the digestive system of a cow, for example, but just at the principal inputs and outputs of the operators (energy and carbon) leaving the details as unknown in a 'black box' analysis.

To summarize, the soil, like any other living system, needs energy. Energy is derived primarily from photosynthesis by plants. It is brought to the soil in three ways: 1) by animals, 2) by litter fall and 3) by plant roots. A further source is the oxidation of minerals by some bacteria. The energy input into the soil is used in driving many reactions involving not only the food chains of many organisms but also the transformations that soil organisms perform on soil components.

4.2 Soil and water

Soil water is fundamental to:
1 plant growth,
2 the growth of soil organisms,
3 the movement of solutes, clays and chelates in the soil.

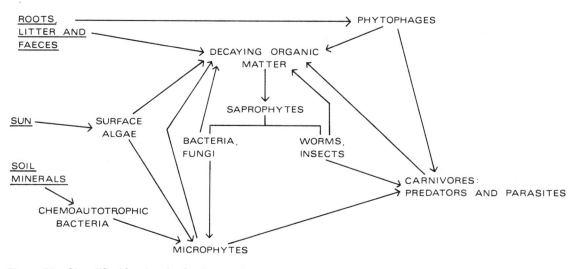

PRIMARY SOURCES   FOOD WEB

Figure 70 Simplified food web of soil organisms

It is possible to think of soil water in terms of soil alone, but it is more interesting to think of it in terms of a stage in the cycle of water in the whole ecosystem.

The hydrological cycle of water is simply the cycle of water evaporating from the seas, lakes and rivers, forming clouds, falling to the earth as rain and then travelling back to the seas again in rivers. But the soil has a fundamental role to play in this cycle. It, like the bedrock underneath it, may act as a *store* for water. If it does not rain for several weeks you can note that rivers usually keep on flowing, albeit at a possibly lower level. They very rarely run dry. This is because water that falls in a rainstorm is stored in the soil and porous rock beneath it, and is released only slowly (Figure 71).

If you imagine rain water falling towards the earth it may be intercepted by vegetation on the way down or it may reach the soil. Some of the water that has been intercepted on leaves and stems of vegetation may evaporate straight back again into the air, but, especially if rainfall is heavy, the water may drip through the leaves as *throughfall* and some may run down the stem. In Figure 72 *interception capacity* refers to the capacity of the vegetation to intercept rain, which obviously depends upon the leaf size and the arrangement of the leaves. *Interception loss* is intercepted water lost by evaporation. Throughfall and *stemflow* apply to the water that actually reaches the soil as a water input. These terms apply equally to water falling on a forest of trees or a field of grass.

Considering now the water that reaches the soil (by direct fall, throughfall or stemflow) the story is by no means over. The water may enter the soil by *infiltration* into the soil pores. Some soils have a relatively impermeable A horizon. This is especially true of compacted soils or eroded soils where hardened layers are exposed. Compact peats and clays are also relatively impermeable. Sandy soils and soils where a loose leaf litter is present allow water to permeate more easily, however. If the A horizon is relatively impermeable it will not be able to transmit all the water that is falling on it and the water remains on the surface. If the surface is flat the water is stored in depressions (*depression storage*) from which it will later either evaporate or seep very slowly into the soil. If the surface is sloping the water may still be stored in depressions, but they may spill over into each other until the water runs overland downhill. Obviously the occurrence of *overland flow* requires rainfall to continue until the infiltration capacity of the soil is exceeded (Figure 73).

If the soil A horizon is permeable (i.e. it has a high infiltration capacity), water can percolate into the soil more readily. Its fate will now depend upon the soil characteristics. The general rule applies, however, that as soon as the water meets a less permeable layer it will tend to back up. The water may only pass vertically down through the bedrock if it is permeable. If the bedrock is impermeable it would flow along the top of it. If it meets an iron pan in the soil it may flow over this. This flow of

53

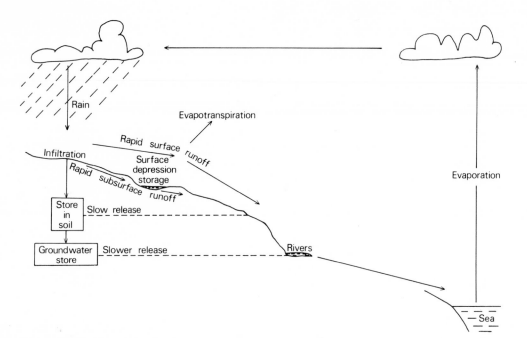

Figure 71　The hydrological cycle

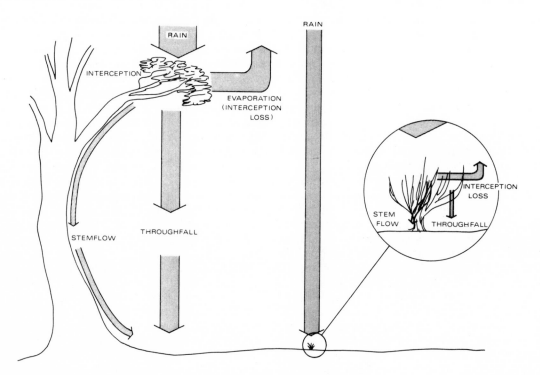

Figure 72　Water reaching the soil

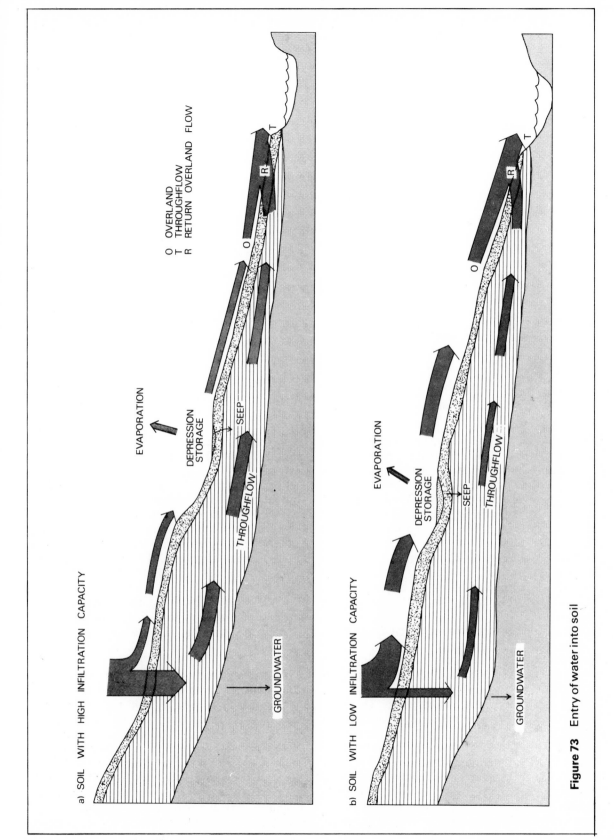

Figure 73 Entry of water into soil

55

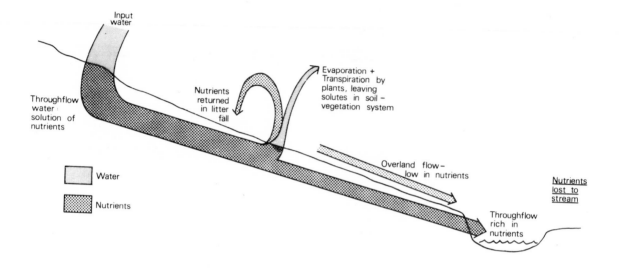

Input water

Throughflow water: solution of nutrients

Nutrients returned in litter fall

Evaporation + Transpiration by plants, leaving solutes in soil – vegetation system

Water

Nutrients

Overland flow – low in nutrients

Nutrients lost to stream

Throughflow rich in nutrients

Figure 74 Nutrients and soil water

water through the soil is termed *throughflow*. It is produced by gravity pulling down the water in large pores but the water being deflected through the soil because of an impermeable or saturated layer. Throughflow water usually flows downslope, but it may flow upwards through the soil to the surface if the soil is very wet. This is termed *return overland flow*.

Throughflow water is important to the development of soil, as it is this water that can carry away solutes downslope and out of the upper layers of the soil. But what is the fate of the throughflow water?

Throughflow water can be of two types: *saturated flow*, acted upon by gravity and flowing in the large soil pores, and *unsaturated flow*, flowing even though all the soil pores are not filled. The latter water flows gently away from areas of high concentration to areas of low concentration. The more rapid saturated flow is more likely to reach the foot of the slope (where there may be a stream or a marsh) and can carry away soil nutrients and perhaps clay particles as a soil output. The line of water flow, or *percoline*, may be subject to the removal of fine soil grains in the water. In wet upland areas natural *pipes* may form by this process, especially in or under peaty horizons. Pipe flow is extremely rapid and soil mineral matter may be carried away
56

by it. The water generally becomes an output of the soil subsystem to become an input of the river subsystem.

The throughflow that passes at a lower speed through the soil may be intercepted by plant roots. In this case the water is drawn up for plant use and the nutrients that are in solution in the water are kept in the soil–plant subsystem and are not lost to the stream subsystem. The nutrients can be returned to the soil at the time of the next litter fall (Figure 74).

The nutrients and small mineral particles lost to the stream or river systems in throughflow water may go to form alluvial deposits, or they may simply be lost to the sea.

In summary, we have seen that soil water is part of a larger cycle of water. Water falling as rain may enter the soil, depending on the interception capacity of the vegetation above it and the infiltration capacity of the soil A horizon. Once in the soil the water may be lost to groundwater in the bedrock or it may move sideways through the soil. The water may be quickly recycled and reused by plants from which it is transpired back to the atmosphere. It may alternatively flow downslope to a stream or river and be returned to the sea, together with some nutrients derived from the soil.

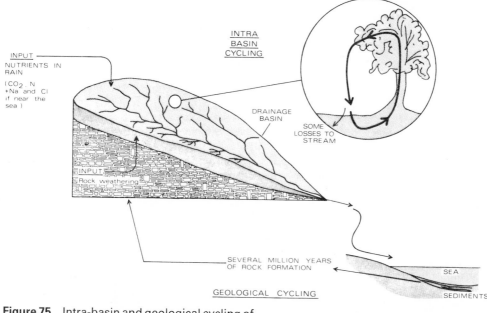

Figure 75 Intra-basin and geological cycling of chemical elements

Soil water is thus part of water in an overall system. The water in the soil subsystem is derived as an output of the atmospheric subsystem. It may then become an output to the plant or river subsystems. No subsystem exists in isolation. All are closely linked by water flow from one subsystem to the next within the overall ecosystem.

4.3 Nutrient cycles

It is a fundamental principle of physics that matter can neither be created or destroyed, but can only change its form. Thus nutrients taken as a soil output cannot be 'lost' but only change their form. They are recycled back to the soil or are moved to another system.

From the descriptions of the inputs and outputs of water in a soil we can begin to build up a picture of how nutrients may be cycled round the ecosystem, moving from plant to organic matter to a clay–humus complex and then back to the plant. Alternatively the nutrients may be lost to the system, for example in a stream. Nutrients lost to rivers in this way are part of a very large geological cycle involving the precipitation of chemicals in the sea, the formation of rocks and the weathering of rocks to release the nutrients again. Nutrients cycled in plants and soils and not immediately lost to streams are undergoing *intra-basin cycling*, that is, cycling within one drainage basin (Figure 75).

Basically nutrient cycling follows the same paths as energy and water flow. Nutrients are released by the weathering of minerals, enter the soil, are used by the plants and animals and return to the soil again. However, some nutrients also enter the soil in rain water and some are fixed from gases in the atmosphere.

It will be useful to consider the nutrients separately, or in small groups, according to the nature of the cycling they undergo. In each case the input and output to the soil is but one link in the chain of linked subsystems in the overall ecosystem. We shall consider two major cycles, the carbon cycle and the nitrogen cycle, and following that the cycling of other nutrients, mainly the commoner cations and anions.

Carbon cycling

We have talked in this book about decomposition of organic matter as one process, soil respiration as another, with photosynthesis and decomposition of minerals as others. As we have already suggested, in the ecosystem these are in fact all linked together. They all form part of a large *carbon cycle* in which the soil plays an important role. We can now piece together the information we already have to produce a picture of the carbon cycle.

Let us begin with the carbon dioxide in the atmosphere. This is thought to have been originally produced from volcanic gases when the world first began and is now used by green plants in photosynthesis to manufacture carbohydrates. The process may be represented by the equation:

$$6CO_2 + 6H_2O \rightarrow C_6H_{12}O_6 + 6O_2.$$

The carbohydrates then reach the soil in plant material using the same paths as were described for energy flow (see section 4.1).

Carbon dioxide is also used in the soil by the autotrophic bacteria that derive nutrition from mineral decomposition. By both this route and the one described in the previous paragraph carbon is 'locked up' in soil humus. One way in which carbon is returned to the atmosphere is by the respiration of the animals that eat the green plants, but a more important step is, however, that of the respiration of microorganisms in the soil. As they decompose the organic matter they respire and act to oxidize the organic carbon and return it to the atmosphere as carbon dioxide, where it may be used for further photosynthesis.

As far as the soil bacteria are concerned these organisms benefit from this process in that they obtain energy for growth and also carbon for cell construction. The carbon dioxide is for them a by-product, but this return of carbon back to the atmosphere for photosynthesis is the basis of carbon cycling in the ecosystem.

Nitrogen cycling

The soil has two inputs of nitrogen – fixation and rain water; and three outputs of nitrogen – denitrification, leaching and cropping. Again, these form components of a larger system of circulation and again, to understand the main operations of the whole process, it is necessary to understand something of the main operators in the system, the soil bacteria.

Starting with gaseous nitrogen in the atmosphere, this is fixed in the soil by a free-living bacteria – *Azotobacter* – and bacterial organisms known as *Rhizobium*. The latter occur in nodules on the roots of leguminous plants (such as peas, alfalfa and clovers). The organisms fix the gaseous nitrogen (N_2) into organically combined nitrogen available as a plant nutrient, either to the plant on which the *Rhizobium* nodule is growing or it may pass into the soil, either as the root dies or when it is ploughed in. Thus the succeeding crop will benefit from the increased nitrogen content. Since nitrogen is the basis of the proteins in the plants this is a vital consideration for plant growth.

The nitrogen may be returned in a number of steps, which may involve a further use by plants but involves three stages of nitrogen transformation from soil humus. The first step is *mineralization* or *ammonification* when ammonia (NH_3) is produced. Under oxidizing conditions this is then changed by *nitrification* by nitrobacteria to nitrate (NO_3) when it may be used by plants. Alternatively *denitrification* may occur where the nitrate (NO_3) is changed to nitrite (NO_2) and is lost to the atmosphere as elemental nitrogen. The denitrifying bacteria, such as those of the genera *Pseudomonas* and *Achromobacter*, obtain oxygen from this denitrification process.

Nitrogen may then be returned to the soil dissolved in rain water or by fixation. An increasing amount is being supplied as fertilizer. The removal of crops clearly takes some of the nitrogen from the soil system, but knowing that nitrate is soluble in water and that water flows as throughflow into streams we can predict that nitrate will also end up in rivers, ponds and drainage ditches. There it may also act as a fertilizer for aquatic plants. This process of nutrient enrichment (*eutrophication*) and the 'blooming' of algae has been noticed in some inland waters in recent years. Farmers are now attempting to minimize this effect by more efficient fertilizer use. Fertilizers are expensive to apply and clearly such losses are uneconomic for the farmer.

Other elements

Cations such as calcium, magnesium, sodium, potassium, aluminium and silica can all be dissolved from soil minerals. They are used as important constituents of plants (grasses, for instance, have a high silica content), and are then returned to the soil in leaf litter. Additions come from nutrients in rain water which can also contain anions, such as chlorine, sulphate and nitrate. Rain is an important source of these nutrients and supplements the supply from rock weathering. A measure of nutrient losses from soil can be gained by measurements of the dissolved load of throughflow waters and also of stream waters.

Summary

It is important to appreciate that soils do not exist in isolation. Nitrate output, for example, 'lost' from the soil, becomes an input to river and bedrock systems. It is important to understand how nutrients are circulated in the ecosystem, especially along the route used by water, both to realize how the nutrients occur in the soil and also to know what effect soil nutrient losses may have elsewhere. It is necessary to place the soil in the context of the ecosystem – the system of linked subsystems – in order to be able to reach this understanding.

4.4 Soil and plants

Soil conditions have a considerable influence on plant growth but often plant growth cannot be thought of solely in terms of soil conditions. Other factors are also involved, such as genetic constitution of the plant, the climate, grazing by animals, competition between different plants and infestation by viruses and fungi. Any one of these factors may limit the growth of plants. It follows that maximising plant productivity, in an agricultural context, or understanding plant distributions, in an ecological context, involves the study of many factors, not simply soil factors. Indeed, for many semi-natural vegetation types man has been the dominant influence on the occurrence of plant species rather than environmental factors. Soil conditions should therefore be seen as one of many contributing factors influencing agricultural crop production and influencing plant ecology.

Plants may also have a significant influence upon soil characteristics. In particular, the nature and acidity of leaf litter can strongly influence the nature of the humus layers in soils which, in turn, act to influence soil properties such as infiltration capacity and acidity. Plants may also influence the nutrient status of a soil, depleting it by nutrient uptake at the roots. Soil is also replenished by the release of nutrients during the decay of leaf litter – including the release of nitrogen which has been fixed within root nodules (see section 4.3).

The soil-plant relationship is thus a two-way one. Soil conditions considerably influence plant growth, along with many other factors, and conversely, plants may modify soil conditions.

The chief soil factors which influence plant growth are:

1 Nutrient supply
2 Soil acidity
3 Soil salinity (in arid and semi-arid areas)
4 Texture and structure
5 Depth available for rooting

Other factors like topography may act indirectly to modify drainage conditions and soil type.

Nutrient supply may limit plant growth. Thus, with any plant and any nutrient there will be an optimum nutrient supply level, below or above which plant growth is hindered by lack of supply on the one hand or possible toxic effects on the other (see section 5.1). Soil acidity becomes a limiting factor chiefly because many elements become highly soluble at low values of pH, often with toxic effects

on plants. Soil salinity may similarly create conditions where plant growth is limited because of the effects of high concentrations of elements and salts in the soil solution.

Soil texture and structure have a marked effect on drainage and aeration. Coarse textured (sandy) soils are well aerated and well drained, but show little water retention. They thus show a proneness to droughtiness in dry weather, when plants will tend to wilt. Fine textured soils (clays and silts) however show a higher water retention capacity but poor aeration and poor drainage, unless they are well structured. Clearly, as with nutrient supply, there is an optimum state and this is represented by a well structured, loamy textured soil showing moderate drainage, aeration and retention of water.

In many cases in soils, the productivity of agricultural crops can be related to the depth of the soil profile. This is because the deeper the soil, the greater the soil volume there is available to supply the plant with nutrients and water, as well as supplying support for the plant. This clearly does not apply, however, in waterlogged or compact soils where, however deep the soil is, plant root growth will be limited.

Nutrient supply

The main limiting factors on plant growth are nitrogen, phosphorous and potassium, (see section 5.1). Of these, nitrogen is often the most important. Here, supplies of nitrogen are independent of mineral sources, that is they are not derived from rock weathering. Nitrogen is fixed from the atmosphere by soil and root nodule bacteria and by some blue-green algae (cyano-bacteria). Nitrogen may also be supplied dissolved in rainwater. These are the only two inputs to plants: the rest of nitrogen is supplied in recycled form from the breakdown of dead plant material or from animal excreta. This emphasises several important factors in plant nitrogen nutrition: firstly, the significance of nitrogen fixing soil organisms and plants such as clover and legumes, in supplying fresh nitrogen to soil-vegetation systems; secondly, the agricultural importance of adding nitrogen fertilizer to augment natural sources and, thirdly, the importance of the breakdown of organic matter in supplying nitrogen. Where organic matter is not replenished by recycling of dead plant material or excreta, nitrogen supplies can diminish in the soil. This will be the case if a crop is grown and the plant products such as leaves, stems, roots or fruits are removed. Nitrogen has then to be replaced by fertilizer (see also p.65). This is especially the case in highly leached soils which are low in organic matter. Under natural conditions, organic material breaks down and the nitrogen released is quickly utilised by networks of plant roots under the leaf litter layer. If the natural vegetation is removed the source of organic matter is lost and the recycled nitrogen is lost. Thus, under these conditions, crops planted on cleared ground rapidly decrease in productivity after 2–3 years, leaving infertile soil. The addition of nitrogenous fertilizer is not necessarily an easy remedy for this since it is costly and, given that the soils are subject to high rates of leaching anyway, in the absence of an efficient root network, the nitrogen will be rapidly lost by leaching. One of the most often quoted cases of this situation is that of the tropical rain forests of central South America, central Africa, and parts of South East Asia. These forests are often best left as natural forests where efficient cycling of nutrients conserves the fertility of the soil.

Phosphorous is derived both from the decay of organic matter and from mineral sources. Thus cycling processes, while important, are not so crucial. Nevertheless, cycling is again often the only source of phosphorous on very leached soils. Phosphorous compounds are most available at around neutral (circumneutral) pH values, being present in the form of low solubility calcium phosphate in alkaline soils and present in the low solubility forms of aluminium or iron phosphates in more acid soils.

Potassium is also available from mineral weathering, especially from minerals such as the potash felspars such as orthoclase or microcline ($KAlSi_3O_8$) form available to plants on exchange sites on clay micelles (see pp.12 and 28). In leached soils, much of the available potassium is bound up in organic cycles.

It is clear that while soil supplies of nutrients may act to limit plant growth, vegetation systems, through recycling, can conserve nutrients when the soil supply is limited. Nitrogen supply and cycling is often one of the most important factors limiting plant growth. Efficient cycling depends upon a flourishing soil fauna which acts to break down plant material. Thus, where waterlogging or acidity discourage soil faunal activity and the breakdown of organic matter by bacteria and fungi, organic matter tends to accumulate without releasing much of its nutrient store. It is, indeed, in such nitrogen poor environments that many of the insectivorous plants occur, augmenting their nitrogen supply from animal sources. In addition, the availability of many of the major elements, and also some of the trace elements used in plant nitrition, is often closely related to soil acidity.

Soil acidity

In acid conditions (see pp.7 and 30), the soil exchange complexes are dominated by hydrogen ions and by aluminium ions. In addition, some other elements, notably iron and manganese, are highly soluble under acid conditions, especially waterlogged, anaerobic acid conditions. Plants which can grow on acid soils are thought to be able to survive under soil conditions where high concentrations of potentially toxic elements occur by the adoption of a number of physiological strategies. One of these strategies is that of reduced transpiration. This reduces the throughput of water in the plant and therefore the uptake of the water-soluble elements also diminished. For example, some of the small leaved heathers (*Erica* spp.) which grow in boggy soils have rolled leaves and low transpiration rates. There may also be exclusion mechanisms at the root surfaces which reduce the uptake of the potentially toxic ions.

Plants which are adapted to survive under acid conditions may, conversely, suffer from a deficiency of some of these elements if grown in alkaline soils. For example iron has a low solubility in alkaline soils. Plants adapted to acid soils, and having an inherently low uptake of iron, may thus suffer from iron deficiency in alkaline soils where there is little iron available anyway; such plants can suffer from a photosynthetic disorder where the leaves become discoloured and yellow, a condition termed *lime chlorosis*.

For many plants the precise adaptations to soil acidity are not fully understood although tolerance to aluminium appears to be important in acid soils whilst ability to take up scarcely soluble iron appears to be important in alkaline soils. However, it is clear that the optimum availability of plant nutrients is in the circumneutral range (see section 5.1). In addition, many plants take up nitrogen in the form of nitrate in circumneutral soils whereas ammonium is the more common form in acid soils; adaptations to soils of differing pH values may therefore be related to the availability and forms of uptake of nitrogen.

Sustained lush growth of plants is often related to a good supply of nitrogen and adequate water supplies. Under these conditions the more robust plant species may compete successfully over smaller species and often rank and lusher vegetation growth dominates in such a situation. By contrast, where nitrate and phosphate supplies are limited, or there are other limiting factors such as climate, a more diverse flora may occur, with a mosaic of smaller species of plants. These would not survive so well under the cover of larger species which would be present if the soil was more fertile. Limestone flora is a good example of this situation. Although rich in lime, the soils are often poor in phosphate and nitrogen as well as often being shallow and droughty. Under these conditions a very diverse community of species may be present in a low growing mat. With more nitrogen and phosphate available, taller grasses and the more robust, vigorous species dominate.

Crops vary in their pH tolerance and the relationships between crop suitability and soil pH can be outlined as:

Alkaline soils (pH 7–8): alfalfa, sugar beet, some clovers, some vegetable crops (lettuce, peas, carrots).

Circumneutral soils (pH 6.5–7.5) as above and arable crops as barley, wheat, maize, rye and oats.

Acid soils (pH 4–6.5): potatoes, some grasses.

The optimum pH for most crops is about 6.5–7, except potatoes which produce best at a slightly more acid pH, about 5. The effect of soil acidity on agricultural crops and the management of soil acidity are considered further in section 5.1.

The acidity of leaf litter may have a discernible effect on the pH of soil, especially in terms of the acidification of soils. The litter of many plants is acid, especially that of ericaceous plants (heaths) and conifers. Thus, the accumulation of such litter may have an effect of acidifying the soil. Part of the processes involved may be the chelation of soil chemical elements by organic compounds derived from the decay of litter. The effect may be pronounced in those soils which are not already highly acid and which do not have a large store of weatherable minerals able to be released to offset the source of acidity from litter. Planting of conifers on soils in the range pH 5–6 thus has to be carefully considered. Above this range minerals will normally be available to offset any effect of leaf acidity. Below this range, leaf litter acidity (often in the range of pH 3.5–5) will be matched by soil acidity and there will be little effect. Within the pH 5–6 range, the acidity of litter may act to solubilise some available mineral elements, encouraging their losses by leaching. A similar acidifying effect will be promoted by acid rain derived from industrial pollution sources, especially from the burning of fossil fuels. This releases sulphates into the air which can form into sulphuric acid in rainwater.

Soil salinity

Soil salinity represents one of the major limiting factors to plant growth on the scarce soil resources which exist in arid and semi-arid areas. As with acidity, the precise physiological mechanisms involved in salt tolerance are not always simple but the relative susceptibility to the soil conditions are fairly well established:

Good tolerance to saline soils	moderate tolerance	poor tolerance
Date palm	Fig	Orange
Barley	Olive	Grapefruit
Sugar beet	Grape	Beans
Rape	Rye	Some Clovers
Kale	Wheat	
Cotton	Oats	
Coconut	Maize	
Sugar cane	Rice	

However, in extremely saline soils, even the more tolerant crops cannot be grown. In order to assess the potential of saline soils, soil salinity must first be measured. Salinity can be measured in an extract of soil water. Salts in water increase the conductivity of an electrical current and so the salinity of water can be measured in mhos (the reverse of ohms, which are units of resistance; the measurement is derived by comparing the actual current transmitted, in amps, at given voltages). The salinity of soil extracts is measured in milli mhos or mmhos per cm (mmho cm^{-1}). The sensitive crops listed above have a restricted yield between 4–8 mmhos per cm (mmho cm^{-1}). The sensitive crops Above 8 only salt-tolerant crops are grown and above 15 mmho cm^{-1} no agricultural crops are liable to give a good yield (Figure 76).

The effects of salt on plants are largely osmotic, effectively restricting water uptake by the plant. During osmosis water will flow from a less concentrated solution, across a semi-permeable membrane such as a cell wall, to a more concentrated solution. In most soils this assists the flow of water from the less concentrated soil solution to the more concentrated cell contents. In saline salts, the soil solution concentration is high and the gradient is reversed; plants thus wilt because their uptake of water is discouraged. In addition to this osmotic effect, plants may also be sensitive to high concentrations of elements which have various toxic effects. Citrus trees, for example are sensitive to high sodium concentrations and develop leaf burn symptoms in saline soils. In other plants,

mmho/cm 0	2	4	8	16
Effect on crop	Effects mostly negligible	Yields of very sensitive crops may be affected	Yields of many crops affected	Only salt tolerant crops yield satisfactorily	Most crops can not be used

Figure 76 Soil salinity values and affects on crops

there appears to be a sensitivity to excess chloride. Salt tolerant plants are adapted to saline soils by various means. They may either restrict their up-take of water and salts, or they may accumulate salt within their tissues; other plants secrete excess salt on their leaf surfaces. Salt contents of soil may be altered by irrigation with water having a low salt content (see section 5.5 p.78).

Other factors: texture, structure, drainage, soil depth

The significance of these factors to plant growth has already been mentioned in earlier Chapters and they will also be discussed in Chapter five. Texture represents one of the more permanent characteristics of the soil which can influence plant growth. Clays are retentive of nutrients while sand particles help to improve drainage and aeration: the optimum combination of sand, silt and clay has already been emphasised. Texture is difficult to alter but its effects can be substantially modified by management, especially by the addition of or-ganic matter and by compaction by stock or machinery or by loosening during cultivation. Similarly, soil depth is a characteristic, which is difficult to alter. Structure and drainage are, however, often modified by man (as discussed in section 5.2 and 5.4).

It can be seen therefore that there are several aspects of the soil-plant relationship. Some factors, such as *texture*, the presence of weatherable minerals and soil *depth* often influence vegetation in a way that is difficult to alter; however, many other factors have a strong influence on vegetation and can also be readily altered by man, notably *acidity*, which can be altered by liming, soil *nutrient content*, which may be altered by fertilizer addition, *salinity*, which may be reduced by leaching with irrigation water and *drainage*, which may be improved. In addition, factors other than soil especially grazing pressure and climate also exert considerable influences on plant growth. The management of the soil factors which can be changed or modified in order to increase agricultural productivity is the subject of the next chapter.

5

Soil management

5.1 Soil fertility

Soil fertility can be defined as the capacity of a soil to consistently produce a desired crop. It is not simply the nutrient supply in a soil. Other soil attributes, such as have been previously discussed (structure, drainage and organic matter content), are also important, both because they influence nutrient availability and also because they are important to plant growth in themselves. Therefore they must all be considered if soil is to be managed satisfactorily to provide conditions of optimum plant growth.

The law of the minimum

The 'law of the minimum' states that the factor which is at a minimum level will control the overall system and this is important for plant growth in soils. For example, it is not useful to have a soil with abundant supplies of nitrogen if the amount of water available is insufficient: crop growth will suffer from a lack of water. Conversely a soil may have a plentiful supply of water but be poor in one or two nutrients. In either case, although the soil may be *generally* fertile, plant growth is limited. *It is the factor in lowest supply (the minimum) which will be the limiting factor in overall plant growth.*

It is therefore important to manage a soil from many points of view and to investigate and understand what the limiting factors are in order to raise the productivity of the whole crop. If water supply is adequate nitrogen supply is usually the most significant limiting factor and therefore nitrogen management is often the most important step in raising crop productivity.

Nutrients

Nine major nutrients are used by plants. These are termed the *macronutrients*. The most important of these are carbon (C), hydrogen (H) and oxygen (O), the others being:

nitrogen (N)
phosphorus (P)

sulphur (S)
potassium (K)
calcium (Ca)
magnesium (Mg)

These macronutrients are the fundamental building blocks of plant tissues and of plant activities. Many other elements are also required in smaller quantities and these are referred to as the *micronutrients* (or *trace elements*). These include sodium (Na), iron (Fe), manganese (Mn), copper (Cu), zinc (Zn), molybdenum (Mo), silicon (Si), boron (B), chlorine (Cl) and cobalt (Co). Other elements, such as vanadium and nickel, have largely unknown, but possibly important, effects. Other trace elements may be picked up by plants, but it is not clear whether they have any important functions and some may even inhibit growth. These include titanium, barium, strontium, chromium, lead, nickel, tin and silver.

In general, since plants take up the water that is present in the soil, they usually absorb the elements that are in solution in the soil water (unless excluded by some mechanism: see section 4.4). Some of the elements picked up are important to the physiological processes of the plant and some are not (Figure 77).

The role of nutrients

Firstly, the plant needs carbon, hydrogen and oxygen for basic cell construction; these being obtained from air and water.

MACRONUTRIENTS
Nitrogen (N) is the basis of plant proteins and is required in large quantities. It promotes rapid growth and it improves both the quality and quantity of leaf crops.
Phosphorus (P) encourages rapid and vigorous growth in seedlings and early root formation. It also hastens maturity, stimulating flowering and seed formation.
Potassium (K) aids the production of proteins and increases the vigour of plants promoting disease resistance and the strength of stems and stalks.

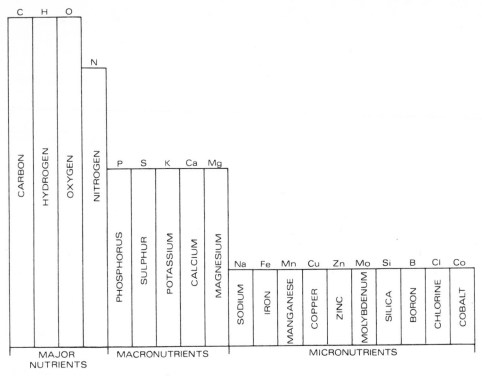

Figure 77 Plant nutrient uptake

It also improves the qualities of seeds, fruits and tubers and helps in the formation of anthocyanin (red colouration) in fruits. It is essential to the formation and translocation of starches, sugars and oils in the plant.

Sulphur (S) is an essential nutrient, more important to legumes, cabbages and some root crops than to cereals and grasses.

Calcium (Ca) is used by root crops. It is most important in the soil for its relationship with soil pH (see below under *Liming*).

Magnesium (Mg) is used in photosynthesis and is a basic constituent of chlorophyll. It is important to arable crops in particular.

MICRONUTRIENTS

Sodium (Na) does not appear to be essential but can increase the yield of grain, roots or fruits produced by a crop. It may be important in osmosis (the transport of water across cell membranes from a dilute to a concentrated solution) and may fulfil some of the roles of potassium.

Manganese (Mn) is used in respiration, protein synthesis and in enzyme reactions.

Copper (Cu) may reduce the toxicity of other elements in large concentrations in the soil and is important in enzyme reactions.

Zinc (Zn) is involved in fruit production.

Molybdenum (Mo) is used in nitrogen fixation.

Boron (B) affects growth.

Chlorine (Cl) may increase the yields of some crops.

Cobalt (Co) appears to be important to some plants, but its function is not clear.

Silicon (Si) is an important constituent of grasses.

Principle of nutrient supply from soils

It is a general principle that for all the essential nutrients there is an *optimum level of supply*. If the nutrient is *deficient* (i.e. there is less than the optimal amount), growth will be stunted, and conversely if the nutrient is in excess, growth will be damaged by toxic concentrations (Figure 78).

The actual optimal value varies for each nutrient. For example, with zinc very small quantities are needed and increasing zinc in the soil from about 50 to 100 parts per million (ppm) helps plant growth, but over 500 ppm zinc is toxic and plant growth suffers. With manganese, up to 500 ppm the plant is healthy but at 1000–2000 ppm the plant's growth is damaged. Below about 20 ppm manganese is said to be deficient because plant growth will be hindered.

The availability of trace elements

Most trace elements (micronutrients) except molybdenum (Mo) are more soluble under acid conditions. Thus in soils of pH 3–5 they are liable to be present in solution in toxic quantities. If the pH is raised to pH 6–7 by liming (see below) they are still available for plant growth but are not toxic.

In alkaline soils the elements tend to be less available and deficiency may occur.

Iron deficiency (chlorosis) may appear on lime-rich soils (see section 4.4). The crops most susceptible to this effect are fruit trees and bushes; arable crops are seldom affected except under extreme conditions. Problem soils may be treated with iron compounds, commonly a substance called iron

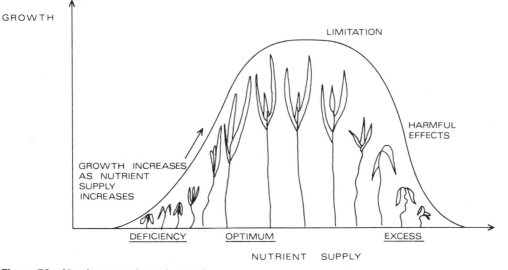

Figure 78 Nutrient supply and growth

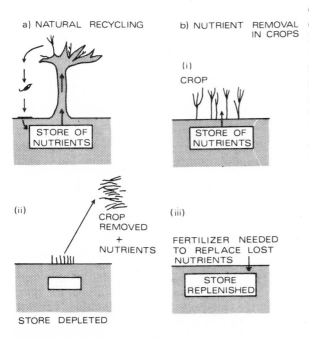

Figure 79 The need for fertilizers

sequesterone. *Boron deficiencies* occur at high pH especially on sandy soils. The susceptible crops include sugar beet, swedes, carrots and lucerne. Boron may be supplied to the soil before sowing. *Copper deficiency* may occur on peats, light sandy soils, reclaimed podzolic soils and thin organic soils over chalk. Crops at risk include cereals, sugar beet and carrots. Foliar spray of copper oxychloride or cuprous oxide may be applied or the soil may be treated with copper sulphate. *Manganese deficiency* can occur on organic soils and sandy soils at high pH. It may also occur on other soils if they are limed too heavily. Most crops are susceptible to this deficiency, especially cereals and many vegetables. Manganese sulphate can be applied either as a foliar spray or a soil treatment. *Molybdenum deficiency* in acid soils affecting some vegetables, is usually corrected by liming or the application of ammonium molybdate. A high molybdenum content of soils (where values rise to around 3–5 ppm in herbage) has the effect of depressing copper availability. This may have an adverse effect on livestock by causing deformities in their bone structures. These problems are more likely to occur on wet, calcareous soils.

65

Sources and losses of nutrients

From our knowledge of soil water and nutrient cycling in the ecosystem (section 4.3) we can list the sources of nutrients as

1 rock weathering – release of minerals from rocks, and
2 the atmosphere – (a) gases and also falling dust; (b) rainwater with dissolved elements, e.g. those from sea spray.

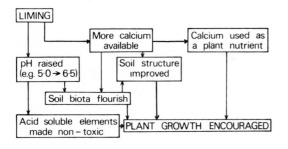

Figure 80 The effects of liming

In natural systems nutrients extracted from the soil are returned in leaf litter for recycling. When a crop is removed this does not occur and the soil's nutrient store will be gradually depleted (Figure 79). In this case nutrients in the soil must be returned by the addition of fertilizers. These have the dual function of *replenishing* nutrients and also *raising* the nutrient status above natural conditions, thereby increasing productivity.

If a crop is not removed, or only partially removed, some of the nutrients are recycled back to the soil and the organic matter content of the soil is also increased. Whilst the ploughing-in of stubble assists in decomposition of the plant material, decomposition itself often takes a very long time (2–3 years) and this is one reason why farmers often choose to burn off stubble rather than plough it in.

FERTILIZERS
Farmyard manure (FYM) can be applied to the soil and this restores the link in the nutrient cycle (Figure 79), by returning animal excreta to the soil. FYM adds nitrogen, potassium, phosphorus and small amounts of calcium and magnesium to the soil. Other trace elements such as copper, cobalt, manganese, molybdenum and zinc may be supplied, depending on the food source of the animals from which the manure is derived.

If natural organic manures are not added to the

soil, fertilizers containing nitrogen, phosphorus and potassium (*NPK fertilizer*) are usually used. These compound fertilizers are common, adding several nutrients at a time. For example 'Nitro-Chalk' adds nitrogen and calcium whilst ammonium sulphate adds nitrogen and sulphur. In each case the soil has to be first analysed for its nutrient content and then the appropriate fertilizer applied to correct for any deficiency.

By replenishing the organic matter in the soil, organic fertilizers add structural processes such as aeration and encourage root growth. Where organic manures are not used it is possible that over several years the organic matter content of a soil may decrease and this may have an adverse effect both on soil nutrient supply and on the stability of some soil structures.

Many arable farmers apply ammonium nitrate, NH_4NO_3, at the start of the growing season in order to boost growth. This supplies nitrogen in two forms, firstly in the ammonium form and secondly in the nitrate form. NPK fertilizer is often applied, either during seeding or later at the initial stages of growth.

LIMING
The solubility of many elements, the growth of plants and the activities of microorganisms in the soil are all dependent to some extent upon the pH of the soil, with the optimum situation being a pH of about 6–7. The addition of lime (calcium carbonate, $CaCO_3$) raises the pH of the soil (see Figure 34, p.31). The *lime requirement* of a soil is *the amount of calcium carbonate needed (per hectare) to raise the pH of an acid soil to a value of between 6 and 7*.

Liming has the follwing effects (Figure 80):

1 it reduces the toxicity of acid soluble trace elements,
2 it improves soil structure, and
3 it increases the availability of calcium as a nutrient for soil organisms and plants.

These effects all help to improve plant growth.
Lime may be needed to counteract the acidity produced by the repeated addition of nitrate fertilizers. Nitrate (NO_3^-) is an anion and as such can combine with nutrient cations such as calcium (Ca^{++}). This may be carried off in solution in mobile soil water in combination with nitrates, and liming helps to counteract this process.

From a knowledge of the relationships between soil pH and crops (section 4.4) it is evident that liming is not a necessary treatment for *all* crops. While arable crops such as barley and sugar beet benefit from a pH corrected to 6–7, other crops such as rye grass and potatoes thrive in a much wider pH range from below pH 5 to above pH 7, with an optimum in the pH 5–5·5 range (see p. 61).

The critical levels of pH at or below which lime should be applied are as follows:

Lucerne, Sainfoin	6.2
Beans	6.0
Barley, Sugar Beet, Pea, Red Clover	5.9
Carrot, Onion	5.7
Rape, White Clover	5.6
Wheat, Hops	5.5
Kale, Swede, Turnip, Cabbage	5.4
Oats, Cocksfoot grass	5.3
Potato, Rye	4.9
Wild white clover, fescue grasses	4.7

Summary (Figure 81)

Nutrients are supplied to the soil dissolved in rain water, by rock weathering, by nitrogen fixation, by recycling of dead plant material and in animal excreta and – in agricultural systems – by fertilizer. Nutrients are lost from the soil by leaching, soil erosion (by wind and water), gaseous losses (especially nitrogen) and losses in crops and livestock; that is plant uptake not returned by recycling. The nutrients perform three main groups of functions:

1 Physiological functions – as a constituent of, or an effect on, enzyme activities and growth.
2 Affects other nutrients, e.g. copper appears to affect availability of other nutrients.
3 Affects soil properties; especially the effect of calcium on solid acidity and structure and also the effect of sodium on the dispersion of clays.

In managed agricultural systems, nutrient losses by leaching soil erosion, crop removal and gaseous losses are offset by management procedures which recycle some nutrients, especially ploughing in unwanted parts of the crop (e.g. stubble), and the application of farmyard manure. The major source of replenishment is the addition of fertilizers. Nitrogen-fixing plants can be grown which increase the soil content of this important nutrient. Fertilizers not only restore the nutrient content of the soil after crop growth but can also be applied to areas of infertile soils in order to reclaim them for agricultural use.

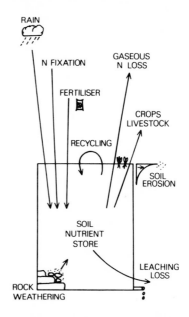

Figure 81 Soil nutrient balance under agriculture

5.2 Soil structure

Basic concepts

The aim of soil-structure management is to produce structures which are suitable for plant growth. As with plant nutrients there is an *optimum level* of structuring. Large, cloddy, persistent structures are as unsuitable for farming as are unstable structures which easily break down into a finely dispersed structureless state. In the former, soil structures are too well established to permit easy root growth, while in the latter the structures are too weak to aid aeration or to permit drainage.

Cultivation and artificial drainage can modify soil structure. The ideal result is a layer of stable crumb structures at the surface, which allows seedling establishment, with a prismatic or blocky subsoil which aids good drainage and helps to prevent waterlogging (provided that the local ground water table also permits soil drainage) (see p.17).

Two concepts of structure are important:

1 structure *form* (shape and size), and
2 structure *stability*.

Form determines packing and pore space and therefore aeration and water retention, whilst stability determines how the structures will behave under ploughing or under pressure from livestock hooves and also the degree to which the structures will break up. The structures should be able to be reduced to a tilth suitable for seed growth and plant

67

establishment, but they should be stable enough not to be able to be reduced to a structureless soil.

Structure form and stability are both related to texture, organic matter content, water content and also, to some extent, nutrient content (see pp. 16–17).

Structure form

In order to understand soil porosity (and therefore aeration and water retention) it is necessary to understand how the texture components (sand, silt and clay) are packed together. Figure 82 shows the unstructured porosity of sand, silt and clay. It can be seen that it is chiefly the size of the pore space between the grains that varies, rather than the total pore space. Indeed the total pore space may be greater in a clay than in a sandy soil, but from a knowledge of how soil water behaves (section 2.7) we know that it is the size of the pore that is most important in determining water retention.

In a soil the particles will be aggregated together by various organic and inorganic cements. They will also shrink and expand according to water content. This causes the organization of the particles

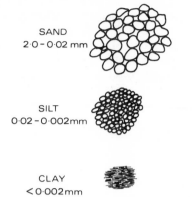

SAND
2·0 – 0·02 mm

SILT
0·02 – 0·002mm

CLAY
<0·002mm

Figure 82 Packing of sand, silt and clay particles

into structures, of which four main types can be recognized (Figure 83):

1 granular or crumb structure;
2 platy;
3 blocky; and
4 prismatic (or columnar if the tops are rounded).

The crumb structures tend to be associated with mixtures of particles in all texture classes and the

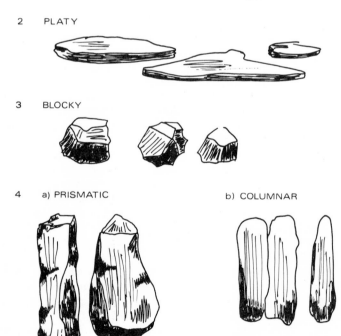

1   GRANULAR (Crumb)

1cm

2   PLATY

3   BLOCKY

4   a) PRISMATIC   b) COLUMNAR

Figure 83 Soil grains grouped in soil structures

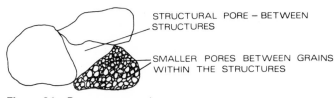

STRUCTURAL PORE – BETWEEN
STRUCTURES

SMALLER PORES BETWEEN GRAINS
WITHIN THE STRUCTURES

Figure 84   Pore spaces and structures

blocky and platy structures with soils having a slightly higher content of silt and clay. The shape of the overall structure tends to reflect the shape of the particles that make up the structure. Thus clays tend to be organized in the longer, narrower structures formed by cracking and compression with alternating shrinkage and swelling.

Variations in the combinations of these structures account for differences in porosity. Two types of pores can be recognized: structural pores and textural pores. The former includes those pores occurring between soil structures and the latter those within soil structures, between the individual grains (Figure 84). Often it is the structural pores which determine the rooting of the plant and the drainage of superfluous water, the inside structures being smaller and holding the reserves of water (see p.22).

Structure packing will determine the amount and size of the pore spaces between the structures. Platy structures will obviously pack very closely and leave little pore space, but crumb and blocky structures can be packed together more loosely given a larger pore space.

Structure stability, drainage and cultivation

Structure stability and soil drainage are closely linked. Structure stability is a limiting factor in plant productivity when either the structures fail to allow good drainage or alternatively where the water table is too high. In either case the soil is liable to be wet when ploughed and a smeared layer of broken-down structures can appear which may lead to the formation of a hard 'plough pan'. The pre-existing structures are unstable when wet and ploughing at the wrong time can break down the structures to give a compact structureless soil layer (Figure 85).

The weight of tractor wheels and livestock hooves can have a similar effect in compacting surface layers of the soil and in the latter case this is known as *poaching*. Platy structures are produced if the soil is subject to pressure when it is wet and the structures are unstable (Figure 86). Basically the weight is causing *compaction* and in both cases

of plough smearing and of weight compaction the soil pore space is reduced. (Figure 87).

Why are some structures more stable than others and why is water content important in determining structure stability? Organic matter, calcium carbonate, aluminium and iron hydroxides and silica all act to cement mineral grains together. Clearly, if a soil has a high content of these then the structures will be more durable and the soil will tend to be more stable. The importance of water content is that many of the cements are soluble in water. Thus, when the soil is wet the cements dissolve and the structures are unstable. When the soil is drier the cements reprecipitate and recement the grains into stabler structures. This is why plough pans form as a hard layer. The cements are weak when the water content is high, but after the soil has dried in dry weather the cements reform and the structures can harden again. Silt soils are particularly prone to structure deterioration as the particles are not cohesive enough to stick together, like clay, nor are they coarse enough to prevent close packing, as in sand. Silt-soil structures may easily collapse as the particles pack closely under pressure. Such soils are usually found over silty parent materials.

The addition of farmyard manure and lime can obviously help to form more stable structures as they will help to aggregate individual particles. But on some soils, for example silty clays prone to structure deterioration, drainage may provide an answer. Drainage can be the most important factor because if the soil is ploughed when wet the soil is more likely to suffer structure deterioration than if the soil is ploughed when drier. Drainage may also influence the amount and nature of iron in the soil, and iron precipitation may be an important factor. Iron is soluble when it is in chemically reduced (waterlogged) conditions, but when the soil is aerated the iron precipitates as ferric oxide, a strong cementing material. Hence drainage of difficult soils may induce the cementation of structures by precipitated iron oxide.

Subsoiling – the breaking up of the subsoil by deep ploughing – greatly improves the overall soil drainage. A well-drained subsoil means that a soil

69

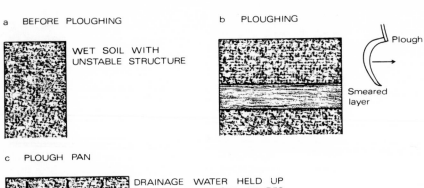

a   BEFORE PLOUGHING

WET SOIL WITH
UNSTABLE STRUCTURE

b   PLOUGHING

Plough

Smeared
layer

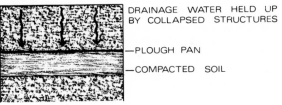

c   PLOUGH PAN

DRAINAGE WATER HELD UP
BY COLLAPSED STRUCTURES

—PLOUGH PAN

—COMPACTED SOIL

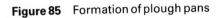

Figure 85   Formation of plough pans

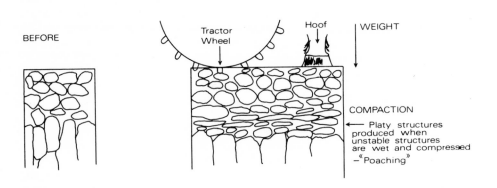

BEFORE

Tractor
Wheel

Hoof

WEIGHT

COMPACTION

←— Platy structures
produced when
unstable structures
are wet and compressed
—"Poaching"

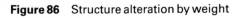

Figure 86   Structure alteration by weight

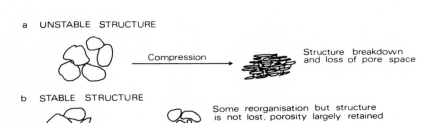

a   UNSTABLE STRUCTURE

Compression →   Structure breakdown
and loss of pore space

b   STABLE STRUCTURE

Some reorganisation but structure
is not lost, porosity largely retained

Figure 87   Pore space and compaction

70

will have few problems of structure stability.

Treatment of the soil may assist in some situations, but the most important step in solving the problem of cultivation on soils with unstable structures is the *timeliness of cultivation*. The right time to cultivate the soil is when the surplus water has drained off sufficiently for the consistency and strength of the structures to be correct. This is when they can withstand the pressures put upon them and will not smear. This time will vary with different soil textures but will be earlier in the year if the soil is well drained (Figure 88).

Soil-structure management can be a delicate problem. The aim is not to try to produce rock-hard cemented structures (similar to those produced when unstable structures are broken down when wet and then set when dry). The aim is in fact to attempt to work out when the structures have their optimum stability for forming a useful tilth for seedling growth.

No one measurement of structure stability is completely reliable in all situations, but a useful idea of structure stability can be gained by applying a force to the structure until it breaks. We can work out, for instance, how many kilograms per square centimetre a cow or a tractor may exert. We can then apply this force to a structure to see if it breaks down. Figure 89 shows one such experiment. By such testing it is possible to estimate both the ideal water content, when ploughing should take place and when to wait for appropriate field conditions.

Structure stability is a much debated topic. Some farmers maintain that ploughing, when wet does their soil no harm (using powerful 'crawler' tractors with caterpillar tracks). Such soils usually include the robust, sandy soils, or those with a high content of cementing agents such as iron, humus and calcium, and they exclude the finer silts and clays, the latter when wet.

Summary

Some soils have structures which are unstable and prone to deterioration under cultivation or intensive stocking with animals. These soils often have closely packed mineral grains and are badly drained. Drainage and the addition of organic matter usually assist in solving the problem, but the timeliness of cultivation is the main way of overcoming the problem.

In many cultivated areas, particularly those with a loamy texture with a high organic content, structure stability is not a problem. Ploughing is used

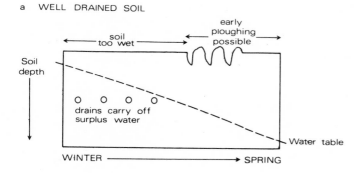

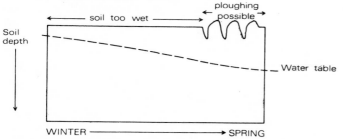

Figure 88   Timeliness of cultivation

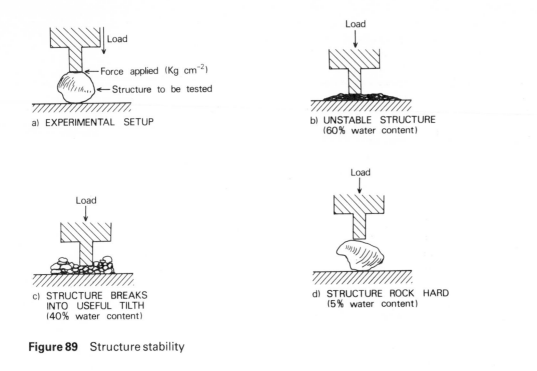

a) EXPERIMENTAL SETUP

Load
Force applied (Kg cm⁻²)
Structure to be tested

b) UNSTABLE STRUCTURE
(60% water content)

Load

c) STRUCTURE BREAKS
INTO USEFUL TILTH
(40% water content)

Load

d) STRUCTURE ROCK HARD
(5% water content)

Load

Figure 89   Structure stability

to return the unwanted part of the old crop to the soil and to expose the soil so that frost and other weathering processes can help to break down the larger structures. This and other treatments, such as harrowing, will render the soil suitable for seedling establishment and crop growth.

5.3   Soil mechanics

The subject of soil mechanics deals with the properties of soils which are important for engineering purposes. Of particular importance are the *load-bearing* properties of soil. When a road is to be built or the foundations of a building are to be laid, it is important for the engineer to know the mechanical strength of the soil and the load which the soil can bear, lest the road slides down a hillside or the foundations of the building collapse.

Also when a dam, or other construction involving water, is to be built the amount of seepage through the soil has to be assessed. Therefore the *permeability* of the soil is often an important characteristic to measure.

Moreover, the load-bearing properties of soils and their water contents are frequently closely related. A wet clay soil is both more liable to flow downhill under pressure, and also to have lower load-bearing properties, than is a drier clay soil.

Soil mechanics, then, concentrates on the mechanical strength and stability of soils which are subject to physical forces. This involves the detailed study of such factors as soil water content, soil permeability, soil plasticity, soil compaction and consolidation, soil particle cohesion and soil movement on slopes.

Engineering definition of soil

Before we can elaborate on these detailed considerations it is first necessary to define what a soil engineer means by the word 'soil' because it is not the same as what, say, an agriculturalist might mean by the term. For the purposes of engineering, soil is considered to be any loose sedimentary deposit; the emphasis being on the word loose, to distinguish it from solid rock. Deposits such as gravels, sands and clays, or mixtures of these, are included. Moreover, it is generally the case that the topsoil is removed before any engineering projects are started. Thus the agricultural and the engineering definitions of soil can be thought of as being almost mutually exclusive. To the agriculturalist the engineer's 'soil' is generally known as the subsoil: to the engineer the agriculturalist's soil, usually distinguishable because it is richer in organic matter than the material beneath, is often removed as a thin layer of unwanted 'topsoil'.

FRICTION AND COHESION

Of prime importance in the study of soil mechanics is the degree of cohesion between the solid soil particles. Particles with highly angular edges and those cemented together by calcium carbonate, iron oxides or clays will tend to be locked together strongly and to be resistant to movements between grains. On the other hand, smooth, rounded individual grains not cemented together, or those well

thin film of water acts to bind the particles together by cohesion. Therefore, in practice, it is necessary to specify the water content of the soil in order to predict its stability.

CONSISTENCY LIMITS

Every small child knows that when earth is puddled with water it forms a delightful mud for making mud pies. But if too much water is added then the

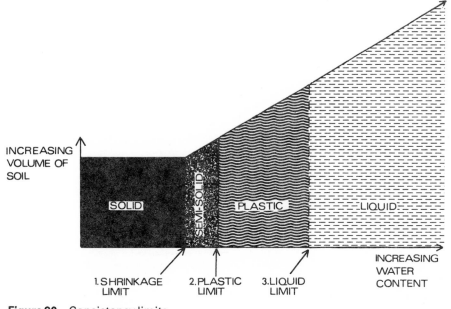

Figure 90 Consistency limits

lubricated by a film of water, will tend to slide over each other, especially when subject to a physical force such as gravity or the weight of a building.

In studying the movement of soil particles it is useful to discuss the two important controls on the physical strength of soils: *friction* and *cohesion*. Friction between particles is greatest, of course, when the surface area of grain contact is largest and when the surfaces themselves are dry and rough. In practice, however, cohesion may be the dominant control. A strongly cohesive soil is one where the individual particles are most firmly stuck together by the cementing agents mentioned above; most important are clays, but iron oxides and calcium carbonate are also significant. But the role of water is perhaps the most crucial. A film of water between particles, if it is thick enough, will act to cushion the particles from one another and thus the lubricated particles can more easily slide over one another with a minimum of cohesion. But a very

consistency of the mud will change till the mixture will flow and the mud pies collapse. Soil engineers attempt to be rather more sophisticated about these matters by the precise specification of *consistency limits*. As water is added to dry soil it passes through the stages of *solid* to *semi-solid* and then to *plastic* and finally to the *liquid* state. Between each of these states a boundary, or consistency limit, is specified and these are defined as follows:

1 *The shrinkage limit* – the limit between the solid and the semi-solid states. Above this limit the soil expands in volume when water is added and is then in the semi-solid state. Below this limit the removal of water causes no further decrease in volume and the soil is in the solid state.

2 *The plastic limit* – the limit between the semi-solid state and the plastic state. As water is added to the soil it becomes plastic and is able

73

to be moulded into shapes. The plastic limit is usually defined more precisely as the minimum moisture content at which the soil can be rolled into a thread of 3 mm diameter without breaking up.

3 *The liquid limit* – the limit between the plastic and the liquid states. At this moisture content the soil will flow under its own weight.

These consistency limits are illustrated in Figure 99. They are also frequently called the *Atterberg Limits* after A Atterberg who first specified them.

the soil. A soil can be subjected to a load and at a certain stage will give way and *shear*, one part of the soil sliding over another. The maximum resistance a soil has to such a shearing stress is called the shear strength.

In coarse-grained soils it is the friction between the grains that is important in determining shear strength. A high proportion of grains which are rough, jagged and interlocking will give a soil a high shear strength, able to bear a heavy load before shearing. In fine-grained soils, however, the cohesion between the grains is the most important

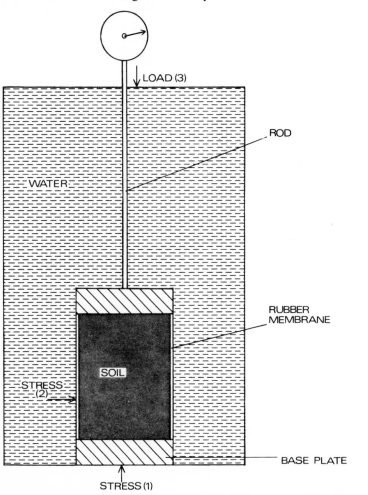

Figure 91 Simplified diagram of the traxial test

Details of the procedures for the determinations of the limits can be found in most standard soil mechanics books (see Further Reading, p. 115).

SHEAR STRENGTH

The load-bearing properties of a soil are usually estimated by measurements of the *shear strength* of

factor. Because of this the water content is a major factor in determining the load-bearing properties of fine-grained soils. Thus fine-grained soils in the semi-solid state will exhibit stronger bonds between the particles and have a higher shear strength than similar soils in the plastic or liquid state.

A common test used in soil mechanics labora-

74

tories to find the shear strength of a soil is the *triaxial test*. The soil sample is stressed from three directions (or in three axes, hence, 'tri-axial') as shown in the simplified diagram, Figure 91. The soil is subject to pressure from 1) the basal plate which is stationary, 2) the water surrounding the soil which is enclosed in a rubber membrane as shown, and 3) the load applied vertically downwards, which is increased until the sample fails, or shears. The load at which the sample fails is recorded. The sample, upon shearing, appears as in Figure 92.

A second test is the *shear box test* which is shown in simplified form in Figure 93. The soil is placed

have large gaps between the slats) and fixing the lower one on to a bench (Figure 94). The upper box should be held down by a large weight (experimentation should show the correct weight, but at least 2–5 kg may be necessary to prevent the upper box lifting at the back and hinging forward at the front). String should be attached to the top box, to which is attached a receptacle for weights. The box should be placed some way back from the bench so that the stress in the top box is as horizontal as possible. Weights can be added to load the upper box until it shears and the load at which shear took place can be recorded. The results gained from such

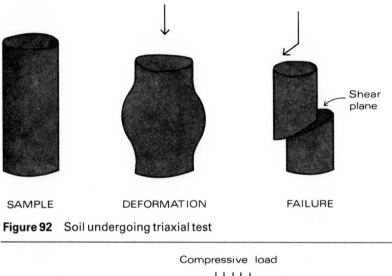

SAMPLE   DEFORMATION   FAILURE

Figure 92 Soil undergoing triaxial test

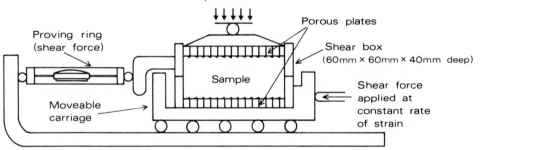

Figure 93 Diagram of a shear box

in a two-part box, the upper half being subject to a force in the opposite direction to the lower. The shear force is increased by cranking a handle until the soil shears. The box is supported on rollers and held in place by a load above. The force being exerted when the soil fails is recorded on the proving ring on the left of the apparatus.

A simpler, cruder, apparatus can be made to demonstrate the principle of shear strength by loading soil into two boxes (e.g. seed boxes that do not

an apparatus will be very crude, and cannot be compared with shear-strength results recorded in the literature, but it can be used to demonstrate the differences between very sandy soils and clayey soils or between wet and dry soils.

PRACTICAL APPLICATION
Many problems of the practical application of soil mechanics can be found in problems ranging from dam building to laying the foundations of buildings

75

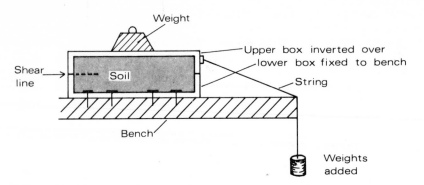

Figure 94 Diagram of a simplified shear-box apparatus

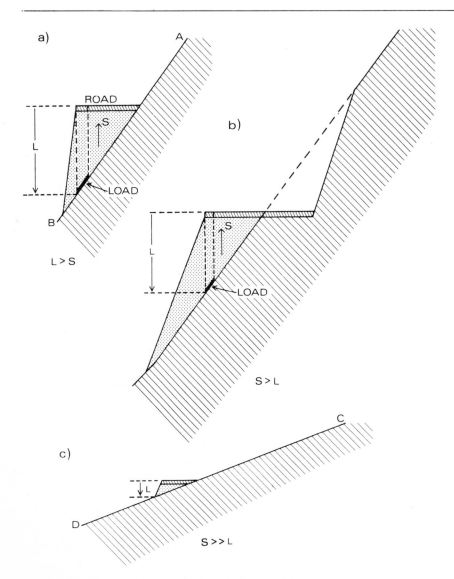

Figure 95 Examples of road construction on slopes

and road construction. As an example, imagine a slope A–B (Figure 90), on which a road is to be built. If a road embankment was built as shown in a) then the load per square centimetre of the original slope is represented by 'L'. If 'L' is greater than the shear strength 'S' opposing it then the road will slide downhill, especially if the soil becomes wet. However, if the road is constructed as in b) so that there is less depth of soil loaded on to each part of the original slope, a decreased load is seen as represented by 'L'. The road is now stable as 'S' is greater than 'L'. This is also true of c) where the slope C–D is much gentler than the slope A–D. This is one

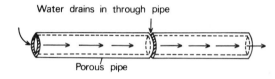

Figure 96 Tile drains

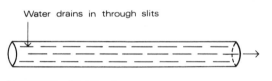

Figure 97 Plastic pipes

hypothetical example of the way in which the measurements of shear strength may be used in the calculation of the slope angle of the embankment necessary to make the embankment stable.

Summary

Soil mechanics deals essentially with the load-bearing properties of soils, defining soils as any loose, unconsolidated material occurring naturally on the earth's surface. These load-bearing properties depend largely upon the properties of each class of soil texture and the water content of the soil because both have a strong influence upon the cohesion between the particles bearing the load.

5.4   Soil drainage

Areas of soil can suffer from excess moisture if:

1 they have a clay texture and poor structures so the water is held in the soil, or
2 they are low lying and the water cannot drain away, or
3 they are in high rainfall localities.

Excess moisture decreases agricultural productivity primarily by decreasing aeration. This, in turn, will have an adverse effect on soil organisms and on plant root development. Usually when a soil is gleyed, drainage could be used to improve the land for agriculture. Earlier methods used either ditches alone or raised ridges between shallow ditches which thus encouraged water to run off. Tile drains, plastic pipes and mole drains are now used widely.

DRAINS

Tile drains are cylindrical pipes of porous clay which have been hardened by firing in a kiln. Each section is laid down adjacent to the next in a trench in the soil and then the trench above the pipe refilled. The depth of drains depends upon a number of factors, including the nature of the soil profile and the desired effect on the water table. The pipes will drain off gravitational water from the soil pores. Various diameters of pipes are used according to the amount of water it is required to draw off, but a common type is 30 cm long and about 10 cm diameter, the porous sides being about 1·5 cm thick (Figure 96). The runoff can be increased by 'backfilling' the drainage trench with porous gravel.

Plastic pipes are a modern substitute, with slots or holes cut in the sides (Figure 97) and it is claimed that these are cheaper and more effective.

Mole drainage (Figure 98) is effected without the insertion of plastic or tile drains. A moling implement is attached to the tractor and pulled through the soil at some depth. This leaves a small tunnel in the soil through which water can drain. The tunnel usually lasts for two or three years, but this depends upon many factors, particularly the soil structure.

DRAIN SPACING

The spacing of drains will obviously influence the amount of water drained from a field and the water table can be lowered more by a closer spacing of drains, as shown in Figure 99. The height of the water table (H) is directly proportional to drain spacing (L). Thus

$$H \propto L.$$

To work out the relationship between (H) and (L) accurately it is necessary to study the rainfall (R) of an area, the permeability of the soil (P) and the depth of the water table to the impermeable layer which is holding up the water (D). Then using the formula

$$H^2 - D^2 = \frac{R}{P} \times L^2$$

77

the amount by which spacing (L) affects the water-table height (H) can be predicted.

The drains are usually laid out in a 'herringbone' pattern with the open end of the pipe being lower down the slope (Figure 100).

Summary
Drainage can be achieved by tile drains, plastic drains or mole drains. The type of drain, the manner in which it is laid and the spacing of the drains are all important considerations in their effectiveness at reducing the water levels in the soil.

5.5 Irrigation and salinity

In areas where evapotranspiration exceeds precipitation soil moisture supplies are often insufficient to sustain plant growth. In order to grow agricultural crops successfully, irrigation may be practiced to overcome this. Water may be drawn

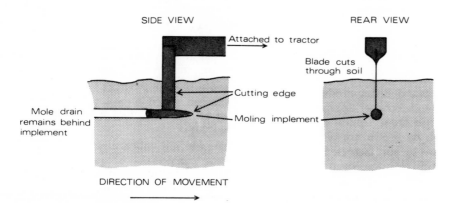

Figure 98 Mole drains

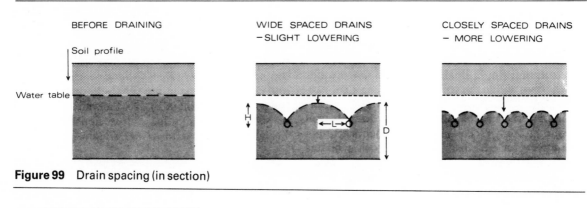
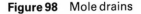

Figure 99 Drain spacing (in section)

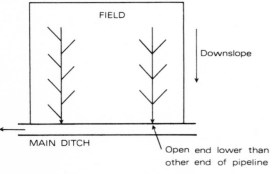

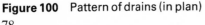

Figure 100 Pattern of drains (in plan)

78

from nearby surface water courses or from groundwater. In either case the quality of water is an important consideration. With the addition of water to soils where evaporation is high any dissolved salts present in the water will tend to be left behind in the soil as the water evaporates. Thus, irrigation in areas of high evaporation can lead to the accumulation of salts in surface soils. This accumulation may be such that it can reduce the agricultural value of the soil (see p.61) and, in severe cases of salt accumulation, prevent the agricultural use of the soil altogether. Water supplies thus have to be carefully monitored for salt content before they are applied. Two main factors are important in irrigation and soil salinity management: 1. irrigation supply should be equivalent to the estimated use of water by the crop in question plus the evaporation loss from any bare soil; 2. the quality of the water applied must be considered.

In terms of the first consideration, water uptake by crops varies according to the conditions of soil moisture and temperature and, also, the stage of plant growth. The extreme ranges of crop use are from approximately 30 cm to around 200 cm water per year, the latter figure occuring in some irrigated desert areas. The common ranges are 40–70 cm water in unirrigated areas and 50–120 cm in irrigated dry regions. Evaporation from bare surfaces again depends on soil moisture and temperature. The relative importance of plant use of water and evaporation from bare soil surfaces obviously will depend on the degree of plant cover. Rates of loss from bare surface may be less than plant loss or, in hot climates, up to three times the figure for plant losses. Total loss may be estimated by the use of an evaporation pan, whereby the water level is topped up daily, the amount necessary to bring the level back up to the rim again being an indication of evaporative loss. Losses via porous cups are also used as a more realistic measure of losses from porous surfaces such as soils or leaves. In addition, a calculated estimation may be used based on a knowledge of the duration of sunshine, temperature, wind speed and humidity, the first three acting to increase evaporation and the last to decrease it. Using these approaches, calculations can be made so that enough irrigation water may be applied to offset evaporation losses. Careful calculation is necessary as over-application may cause unnecessary leaching of plant nutrients below the root zone; under-application may mean that excess salts may not be leached away fully and will accumulate in the soil.

The second consideration, that of water quality, is as vital as the first. The salinity of the applied water should be as low as possible as, even with careful calculation of the amount of water to apply, a high salt content in water will lead to salt accumulation in the soil. This is because some of the irrigation water will evaporate, leaving salts in the soil. Salinity is measured in terms of electrical conductivity, in units of electrical conductivity, in units of mmho cm^{-1} (see p.61). Irrigation waters are classified in terms of salinity as follows (in units of mmho cm^{-1}):

Class 1	Class 2	Class 3	Class 4
LOW	MEDIUM	HIGH	VERY HIGH
<0.25	<0.75	<2.25	<2.25

Classes 1 and 2 are preferred, class 3 is the maximum used in normal practice. Given these limits and assuming adequate drainage to facilitate the leaching of salts, the amount of irrigation water to be added to allow for the salt content of the water is calculated using the leaching ratio, R:

$$R = \frac{CI}{CD} \times 100$$

where CI = conductivity of irrigation water and
CD = conductivity of the drainage water

The value of R, which is a percentage term expressing the way in which salts are being concentrated in the soil, is added to the amount of water already calculated to offset plant use and evaporation, as discussed above. Thus if CI = 2 mmho cm^{-1} and CD = 20 mmho cm^{-1} then:

$$R = \frac{2}{10} \times 100 = 10\%$$

thus the application of water is 10% in addition to that already estimated to replenish crop use and bare soil evaporation. Additionally, as well as soil salinity, tests may also have to be carried out on the trace element concentrations in irrigation water to ensure that no harmful substances are being added. This may preclude the use of certain water supplies altogether.

Many soils have been salinised in the past by the use of irrigation waters of too high a saline content, or by inadequate irrigation in very dry areas. This has reduced their agricultural value or prevented agricultural use altogether. Such problems are becoming rarer as it is realised that they can be avoided if detailed attention is paid to the considerations outlined above.

5.6 Soil erosion and conservation

Basic concepts

Soil erosion is usually thought of as the removal of the solid particles of the soil, either by wind or by water. However, it also includes the removal of nutrients and clay colloids in solution in the water which flows within the soil matrix. While solid particle erosion has been recognized as a problem for some time the loss of nutrients as a form of soil erosion has only recently received much attention. The latter is referred to as 'chemical erosion' or 'fertility erosion' as it represents a potential loss in agricultural productivity by a depletion of the store of soil nutrients. Furthermore, awareness of this problem is necessary to tackle the problems of eutrophication of inland waters (see section 4.3), because the loss of nutrients from the soil may represent a gain in nutrients in ponds, ditches and rivers. This may lead to the 'blooming' or sudden multiplication of algae detrimental to the aquatic life.

Soil erosion can occur in one of three ways:

1 the physical detachment of soil particles and the washing of soil downslope and down gullies or in sub-surface pipes;

2 the physical blowing of topsoil away in strong winds, and

3 the chemical loss of nutrients in solution by leaching.

Erosion by rainfall and surface wash

Raindrop erosion is at its most effective on bare cultivated soil where rain drop impact can detach particles of soil and splash them into the air. On sloping surfaces this encourages the downslope movement of particles under the influence of gravity. This process is further encouraged by the occurrence of surface wash. (see below). It is important to distinguish between erosivity and erodibility. *Erosivity* refers to the potential for erosion supplied by the energy of rainwater; *erodability* refers to the propensity of the soil to be eroded. Highly erosive rains and highly erodible soils combine to give the greatest erosion. Heavy rains falling in a short space of time are more erosive than gentle rain; weakly structured fine sandy and coarse silty soils are more erodible than soils composed of larger and heavier grains or soils composed of finer cohesive clays where the particles stick together (see below, under wind erosion).

Erosivity is related to the amount of rain falling in given time periods; this is termed the *intensity* of rain and it is usually measured in mm h^{-1}. More intense rain has a greater kinetic energy and is more capable of detaching soil particles on impact with the ground. Indices of erosivity which are used to predict soil erosion frequently involve a study of the maximum intensity of rainfall occurring during a storm. When calculating erosivity for a storm, or on an annual basis, the gentler rainfall events (those less than 25 mm h^{-1}) are normally discounted as being ineffective and only the heavier rainstorms are considered. In temperate areas, commonly only 5% of rainfall events fall above this threshold, while in tropical areas, more intense rainfall occurs and commonly 40% of the rain is above this threshold. Tropical rainfall intensities may rise to 150 mm h^{-1}, with a correspondingly greater kinetic energy available for erosion. Tropical rain may possess a kinetic energy of up to 15,000 joules m^2a^{-1} while a comparable figure for temperate areas would be around 1,000 joules m^2a^{-1}. Although the figures for temperate areas are considerably lower than those in the tropics, this is not to underestimate the significance of soil erosion in temperate areas, which can be considerable, especially on the lighter, fine sandy soils.

Surface wash is an important consideration in both temperate and tropical areas. Rainfall intensity again plays an important part in the occurrence of surface wash. Intense rain is less able to infiltrate into the soil-surface than is gentle rain. This is because the soil has a maximum infiltration rate which is governed by the sizes of the soil pores opening at the surface (see p.53). If rainfall intensity is greater than infiltration rate then surface runoff will occur. Particles detached by rainsplash or the flow of the runoff itself will be moved downslope in the surface wash. The amount of wash will build up downslope, often leading to greater removal towards the midslope; towards the base of the slope the maximum sediment carrying capacity of the water may be reached so that no further erosion will occur. Slope steepness also encourages wash by increasing runoff velocity.

Soils at risk include those which have a low cohesiveness and the less well structured fine sands. In the case of silt sized soils, aggregation by organic matter and inorganic cements such as iron and calcium increase the size of structures and decrease the risk of erosion. In finer soils, however, aggregation may mean that while the individual particles were small and cohesive, and therefore unlikely to be eroded, the aggregate size may be such that the aggregates are of silt size and thus more easily moved.

Erosion by rain and surface wash can then be seen as related to:
1 Rainfall energy and erosivity,
2 Soil type and site characteristics such as slope.

Management activities influence aggregate size, crop cover and the amount of bare ground which can be acted upon by erosive forces. Management may thus act to decrease soil erosion by increasing the amount of cover and taking care with cultivation practise.

Slope processes

If old fields on slopes are studied carefully it may be noticed that the soil is at different levels on either sides of hedges and banks running across the slope. The soil is higher on the upslope side and lower on the downslope side (Figure 101). On the upslope side soil has accumulated by surface wash and soil creep. These processes are known as *colluvial wash* or *colluvial movement* and the resultant material is *colluvium*. These are natural processes and will occur to some extent even under a close grass cover, especially where the slopes are steep and the rainfall is high. The processes may be accelerated by ploughing on steep slopes. Runoff may be rapid after rainstorms, and the accumulations of water-washed sediments may be seen at the foot of fields after storms. In general the overall effect may be to damage the soil as the topsoil is lost from the upper part of the field and buried in the lower part of the field, but over all, the slope will tend to become gentler (Figure 102).

Soil erosion on slopes can usually be minimised by not ploughing on steep slopes and leaving the soil under grass. The problem can be minimized, and the soil conserved, by ploughing across the slope, along the contours, rather than straight up and down the slope. With contour ploughing the water seeps through the ridges and does not build up enough momentum to carry soil with it (Figure 103).

Soil erosion on slopes may be a particular problem if drainage ditches are installed up and down the slope in order to achieve maximum runoff. In the early stages of forest growth, before trees ameliorate the effects of rainfall, this arrangement gives the water maximum erosive power and some soil erosion may result bringing sediment down into streams and rivers. Similarly, gulleying and piping may develop naturally, acting to conduct water and sediments rapidly downslope. Here, the blocking of gullies may be an effective conservation measure and the breaking of the runoff zones into small units of short length is important so that water cannot build up momentum and achieve its maximum sediment transporting power. Soil conservation engineering works are best achieved by simple methods that can be used extensively and cheaply and which require little maintenance. The frequent use of earth banks, hurdles of vegetation and wire baskets filled with stones (termed *gabions*) stacked together are often far more effective than the less frequent use of more costly concrete engineering works. In addition, sensible land use, that is lack of cultivation on the steepest slopes, or an effective terracing system on steep slopes, is fundamental to effective soil conservation (see section 5.7 p.84).

Wind erosion

Wind erosion of topsoil occurs where large open areas exist. Fine sands and silts may be winnowed out of a dry soil if a bare exposed surface is left after ploughing.

Not all soil grains are as prone to wind erosion as others. The larger sand grains are too heavy to be moved, except by the strongest winds. Clays, on the other hand, although in themselves small enough to be blown away, possess the important property of cohesion (see section 2.4), sticking together and thus being resistant to wind erosion. Silts are the most prone to wind erosion as they are small enough to be blown and yet possess no cohesive properties. The strength of wind needed to move a soil particle of a particular size is shown in Figure 104.

In open fields wind can select the erodable soil fraction (mainly the finer silts) and leave behind the coarser soil structures and stones. Silt may accumulate on field edges and banks (Figure 105). This is particularly common where hedges have been removed.

Well-planned shelter belts are an important way of managing soils liable to wind erosion. Shelter belts can reduce wind strength, depending upon the type of belt used. Trees with a low barrier of bushes are the most effective (Figure 106). Closely spaced shelter belts are the best protection against physical soil erosion in arable areas. On the other hand it is often more economic to have larger fields and thus be able to use efficiently large agricultural machinery, such as combine harvesters. Whether or not a hedge is grubbed up or a shelter belt is planted must be a matter of balancing the economics of having large mechanized field systems against losing money by crop deterioration resulting from soil erosion. It is also important that the shelter belts act as reserves for wild life, which

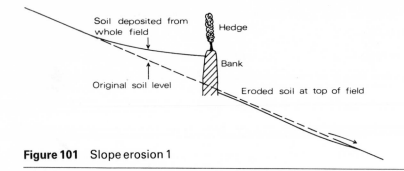

Soil deposited from whole field

Hedge

Bank

Original soil level

Eroded soil at top of field

Figure 101   Slope erosion 1

BEFORE EROSION

AFTER EROSION

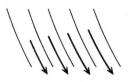

A

B

C

Eroded soil

A

Sediment

B

C

Figure 102   Slope erosion 2

a   Ploughing up and down slope encourages erosion

b   Contour ploughing minimises erosion caused by running water

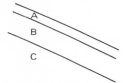

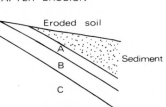

Figure 103   Ploughing on a slope

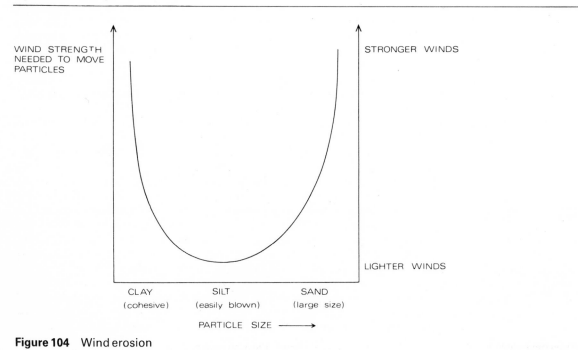

WIND STRENGTH NEEDED TO MOVE PARTICLES

STRONGER WINDS

LIGHTER WINDS

CLAY
(cohesive)

SILT
(easily blown)

SAND
(large size)

PARTICLE SIZE ⟶

Figure 104   Wind erosion

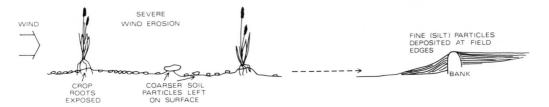

Figure 105 Wind erosion in open arable fields

itself has some significance to crop growth. (For example, hedges act as habitats for birds which are important in reducing insect pest numbers.) Also one needs to balance long-term costs of the possible alternative management schemes (open fields *v.* shelter belts) and decide the best policy.

Chemical erosion

Leaching has already been discussed under the headings of soil development, nutrient cycling and soil fertility (sections 3.1, 4.3 and 5.1). Leaching not only represents chemical loss in itself but it may also lead to the physical weakening of soil structures. This is because chemicals which cement soil structures may be lost. If large structures break down they are more susceptible to wind or water movement.

Where the dominant water movement is downwards, under adequate rainfall (i.e. where rainfall exceeds evaporation), nutrients will be dissolved and washed down from the topsoil. Natural pipes, such as are found in and under peat in upland areas (see section 4.2), also encourage this process.

Chemical analysis of waters flowing out of tile drains shows that calcium, sulphate, chlorine, nitrogen (in the form of nitrate) and sodium are the most readily lost nutrients. Magnesium, potassium, phosphate and nitrogen (in the form of ammonium compounds) are also lost, but in lesser amounts. Much of these nutrient losses may, in fact, come from applied fertilizer, although in some cases the origin is from rock weathering or, especially in the case of chlorine, from rain water. It is possible that in many cases too much fertilizer is being applied to the soil and the excess is being lost in drainage waters. Clearly, in marshy areas the nutrients would be retained in the soil if the tile drains were not installed, but the soil would be too wet to be of much value.

In high rainfall areas with natural free drainage there is little that soil management can do to prevent leaching losses. It must ensure, however, that:

1 artificial drainage is not too excessive, i.e. runoff is not more than it need be for adequate crop growth, and
2 excess fertilizer (which costs money) is not applied.

Summary

The agents of physical erosion are water running over the surface and wind. The problems of soil erosion can be curbed, or avoided, by not ploughing on steep slopes and by the use of shelter belts to protect those soils with a texture prone to blowing (chiefly those having a silt texture). Chemical erosion includes natural leaching and the leaching of applied fertilizers. Careful calculation of correct fertilizer application minimizes the chemical

a) OPEN BELT
LITTLE WIND REDUCTION
SOME TOPSOIL EROSION

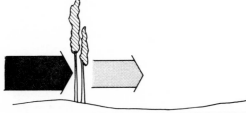

b) THICK BELT
GREATER WIND REDUCTION
LITTLE TOPSOIL EROSION

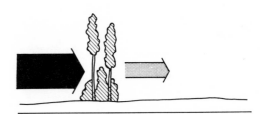

Figure 106 Shelter belts

83

erosion of fertilizers into inland waters.

5.7 Soil resources

With a high population there is an incessant demand on the land to produce food. This is made more difficult in urbanized countries by the demand for building land which encroaches upon agricultural land, but some land is obviously more suitable for agriculture than others. Soil can sometimes withstand intensive cultivation; in other situations it may not. The proper and full use of our soil resources needs the understanding of how a soil works and a knowledge of the capability of soil in agricultural production. In this way the land available for agriculture is made the most productive to meet the demands of society for food.

Land capability

Soil erosion can be avoided, soil fertility and structure maintained and yields improved if a soil is not cultivated beyond its capability. For example, a valuable, deep, fertile loam, with a high organic matter content, a neutral pH, stable structures and adequate drainage in a region with moderate rainfall, can grow a very wide variety of crops with profit and without any damage to the soil. It is a versatile soil with a high capability. On the other hand a less fertile soil on a steep slope has a low capability and the crops that can be cultivated with profit are limited. Attempts to grow wheat on such a soil might show little profit and may cause damage to the soil by slope-wash erosion. The capability of the soil would probably limit its agricultural use to grassland.

While the physical capability of the soil is a major constraint on soil productivity it should always be remembered that economics usually govern what is grown. Therefore, if, in the case of the steep slope mentioned above, there was a tremendous demand for wheat and it fetched an extremely high price it might possibly be profitable to terrace the slope and contour plough to stop soil erosion. In this case, wheat could be grown with profit because of the economic demand for it. This is obviously an extreme example, but physical limits are only important when related to economic factors. The crucial factor is whether the cash benefits gained from managing difficult lands are greater than the cost of improving the land for agriculture.

Systems for land capability classification

Several national and international schemes for

land capability classification have been proposed. Selected examples of these are outlined below: the US Soil Conservation Service scheme, the UK Soil Survey Scheme, the UK Agricultural Land Classification scheme and the International FAO scheme.

THE US SOIL CONSERVATION SERVICE

The classes are numbered from I to VIII. Soils with the least limitations and the greatest potential for productive management are termed class I. These may be used for the most intensive agriculture as well as all the other uses to which the lower classes can be put. The soils are deep, well drained and fertile on level sites, showing a good response to ordinary management practices. In general, there is no risk to the soil resource if it is used for agriculture. Successive lower classes impose greater restrictions on agriculture and there is a greater risk of the degradation of the soil resource if the land is used outside its capability. For example, soils on steep slopes are given a lower classification with recommendations for use in terms of grassland, forestry or wildlife conservation. Use of this class of land for cultivation, that is use *outside its capability,* can lead to severe erosion. Use of land within its capability is therefore an important prerequisite of sensible soil conservation.

An outline of the class is as follows:

Class I. Little limitation. Intensive agricultural use.

Class II. Slight limitations. Intensive use with some care because of factors such as moderate slope, slight limitations of depth, structure, salinity or drainage.

Class III. Severe limitations. Only moderate cultivation use. Steeper slopes, erosion hazards or moderate limitations of those factors already mentioned in Class II.

Class IV. Only just suited for cultivation, severe limitations due to factors already mentioned; soil conservation measures are fundamental if cultivation is practiced.

Class V. Not suited to cultivation. May be suitable for pasture improvement; problems of climate, steepness, stoniness or other limitation.

Class VI. Extreme limitations, possible use as pasture.

Class VII. Best used for wildlife conservation or recreation.

It should be emphasised that the uses suggested for each class can be put into practice for the classes higher than recommended (e.g. wildlife conservation on Class V or IV) but they should not be used

a) DISTRIBUTION OF LAND CAPABILITY

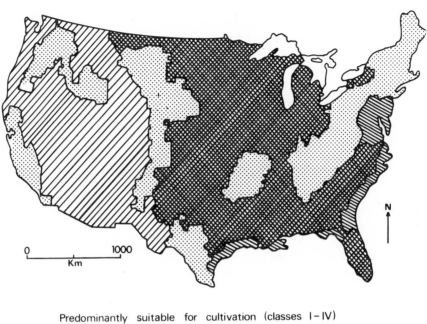

Predominantly suitable for cultivation (classes I–IV)

More than 67 percent suitable

50–66 percent suitable

Predominantly unsuitable for cultivation (classes V–VIII)

More than 67 percent unsuitable

50–66 percent unsuitable

b) SUGGESTED USES

CLASSES I–IV			CULTIVATION
CLASSES V–VIII	WILDLIFE RECREATION FORESTRY	PASTURE	

Figure 107   Land capability in the U.S.A.

for classes *lower* than recommended (i.e. no cultivation on class V land). The distribution of land capability classes in the USA is shown in Figure 107.

UK SOIL SURVEY SCHEME

This scheme is similar to the USA scheme, with 7 classes, though there is less concern with steepness and soil erosion as this is less of a problem in the U.K. However, the same limitations are recognised as in the USA: wetness, soil type, gradient, climatic and erosion risk.

The classes:

1 Very minor or no limitations
2 Reduced choice of crops, some interference with cultivation
3 Moderate restrictions on crops, careful management needed
4 Severe limitations, very careful management
5 Restricted to pasture, forestry, recreation
6 Very severe limitations: rough grazing, pasture, forestry
7 Land with very severe limitation which cannot be rectified.

UK AGRICULTURAL LAND CLASSIFICATION SCHEME

An alternative land classification for the U.K. is provided by the Agricultural Land Classification scheme of the Ministry of Agriculture, Fisheries & Food. The highest grade, Grade 1, is extremely versatile and is capable of growing a wide variety of crops. Lower grades are more restricted in use, but their capability can be improved by, say, irrigation or drainage, if this is economically desirable. Since the management and economic factors are variable the classification is based on physical factors that limit agriculture under an *average* management scheme.

Agricultural land classification

Land in Britain has been grouped by the Ministry of Agriculture, Fisheries and Food into capability grades in an *Agricultural Land Classification*. The highest grade, Grade 1, is extremely versatile and is capable of growing a wide variety of crops. Lower grades are more restricted in use, but their capability can be improved by, say, irrigation or drainage, if this is economically desirable. Since the management and economic factors are variable the classification is based on physical factors that limit agriculture under an *average* management scheme.

Land is graded according to the limitations that soil, slope and climate impose on agriculture:

Grade 1: No physical limitations. Deep well-drained loams, sandy loams, silt loams or peats. Level or gentle slopes. Nutrient rich. Wide range of crops with high yields. Any arable or horticultural crop can be grown.

Grade 2: Some minor limitations. Factors make the land slightly less flexible in the choice of crops that can be grown economically, e.g. texture, drainage, depth and climate. Most arable and horticultural crops can be grown.

Grade 3: Land with moderate limitations due to soil, relief or climate. Factors such as stoniness or altitude may limit productivity. Grass and cereals can be grown. Grade 3 land includes some of the best grasslands but is marginal arable land.

Grade 4: Severe limitations, e.g. unsuitable texture and structures, surface wetness, shallowness and stoniness, steep slopes, high rainfall or exposure. Mostly used as grassland, but some poorer crops of oats and barley can be grown.

Grade 5: Little agricultural value. Very steep slopes, very poor drainage, excessive rainfall and exposure, severe plant nutrient problems. Forestry and rough grazing are the usual land uses.

In much of Britain, where factors such as stoniness and depth are not limiting, texture and drainage impose most of the restrictions on agriculture. Clearly the significance of drainage depends upon the amount of rainfall, but assuming a constant rainfall in one region the grades would be distributed in that region according to texture and drainage. Grade 4 land occurs where drainage is excessive or very poor. Grade 5 occurs where the rainfall is higher or the slope steeper or the soil is in a flat marshy area near sea level. In the case of the heavier soils (clay textures), as drainage improves so the capability of the land improves, but Grade 1 is rarely achieved. With the lighter, sandier textures moderate drainage is the optimum but excessive drainage leads to drought susceptibility. The optimum soil is clearly a moderately to well drained loam.

With irrigation a sandy soil prone to drought may be raised from Grade 4 to Grade 3 and some sandy soils in East Anglia are in this category. With drainage a clay soil may similarly be raised from

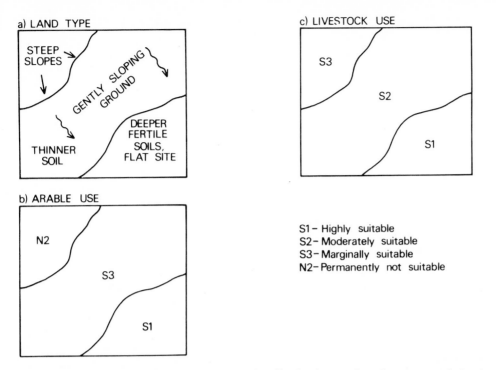

Figure 108   FAO scheme of land classification (for further explanation, see text below)

Grade 4 to Grade 3. For this reason a Land Capability Class may be quoted as 4(3), indicating that under better than average management the land capability can be increased.

Land capability maps are produced and they can be compared with soil maps. The capability units may be larger than the soil units as two soil types may have the same capability.

THE FAO SCHEME

The schemes outlined above assume a moderate input of management. The United Nations Food and Agriculture Organisation (FAO) scheme does not necessarily assume this and makes a distinction between firstly, suitability under current conditions, which may alter in the future, and secondly, suitability which is unlikely to alter and may be considered permanent. The scheme therefore recognises a conditional suitability, where land might be suitable under a different management technique, for example with better drainage or irrigation. There are two main orders:

S – *Suitable land:* sustained use will yield satisfactory yields without putting the soil resource at risk. ('Satisfactory' means that the benefits are commensurate with the management input levels).

N – *Not suitable.* Sustained use is not desirable in terms of lack of satisfactory returns and/or future degradation of the soil resource. The order S had a suborder Sc, *conditionally suitable* under different management.

Suitable land (Order S) is subdivided into 3 classes:

Class S1: *Highly suitable.* No significant limitations to sustained use.

Class S2: *Moderately suitable.* Limitations exist which reduce productivity.

Class S3: *Marginally suitable.* Expenditure is only marginally justified because of limitations.

Unsuitable land (Order N) is subdivided:

Class N1 – *Currently not suitable:* – land having limitations which could eventually be surmounted in the future.

Class N2 – *Permanently not suitable* – Land having limitations which are so severe as to permanently preclude use.

Land can be classified for suitability of any given land use. Thus, the suitability may be (a) for arable use, (b) for livestock farming, (c) woodland, (d) conservation, and so on. Different maps are thus produced for the same area for different potential uses. This is illustrated in Figure 108.

Land capability and crop production

Research on this topic varies in its completeness.

87

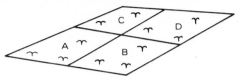

a) EXPERIMENTAL PLOTS

b) YIELD MEASUREMENT

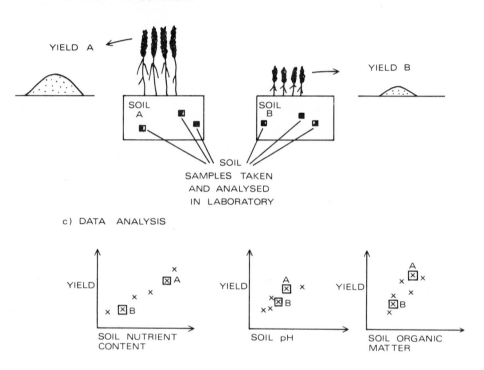

YIELD A

SOIL A

SOIL B

YIELD B

SOIL SAMPLES TAKEN AND ANALYSED IN LABORATORY

c) DATA ANALYSIS

YIELD — SOIL NUTRIENT CONTENT

YIELD — SOIL pH

YIELD — SOIL ORGANIC MATTER

PLOTTING SAMPLE DATA ON GRAPHS DEMONSTRATES ANY RELATIONSHIPS BETWEEN CROP YIELD AND SOIL CHARACTERISTICS

Figure 109 Crop trials

Some examples of land capability and crop production can be given and other cases can be discussed where the relationships between soil resources and crops is broadly known. As an example, crop yields on the different grades of the UK Agricultural Land Classification System can vary as follows:

Grade	Wheat yield*	Sugar-beet yield*
1	5000–5500	6000–8000
2	4000–5500	5000–6000
3	3000–4000	4500–5000
4	Uneconomic	c. 4000
5	Uneconomic	Uneconomic

*Yields in kilograms/hectares of grain for wheat, roots for beet

It is difficult to propose general rules about crop yields, soil type and land capability, and crop trials are the main way of experimenting with crop productivity on various soil types (Figure 109). Experimental plots can be laid out and sown with identical seed, the yield from each crop measured and the soil on which the crop was grown can then be analysed. Information about the relevant soil attributes can be plotted against yield and the reasons for different yields examined. By careful soil study the productivity of a piece of land can be estimated by assessments of soil type and of the overall land capability (including factors such as slope and climate).

In this way the agricultural scientist and soil scientist can combine their skills to work out the factors which influence the productivity of a crop. By using land capability assessments, advice can be given as to the best crop for a particular area.

Examples from tropical soils show that yields are related to soil quality and that careful management is often necessary. In Malaysia, highly leached soils are used for rubber and oil palm. Research has shown that for soils cleared from forest, much of the fertility is derived originally from residual organic matter; subsequently, high productivity can only be sustained by fertilizer input. Similar results have been obtained from many parts of Africa, though the crops used differ. In Nigeria, cocoa and oil palm are important crops. Again, productivity is increased by fertilizer use, soil physical characteristics may then act to impose limitations once fertility levels are adequate. In many cases, low nitrogen levels impose limitations on crop growth and this stresses the importance of the use of nitrogen fixing plants. Soil structural stability and the occurrence of trace elements also impose limitations. In the study of soil type, land capability and crop growth, it is important to distinguish between these site and soil characteristics which can be easily altered and those which are more permanent. Land capability often only refers to the latter while crop growth is often more sensitive to the former factors, especially the nutrient supply which can be readily altered by fertilizer addition. Thus, it is important to remember that land capability refers to the less changeable characteristics and to moderate management inputs. The study of crop growth and soil conditions at a more detailed level may show many variations within one land capability class. Basically, the idea of land capability is to promote sensible land use planning in broad terms, in particular to promote the use of the best land for cultivation and to encourage the maximum use of soil conservation practise.

Summary

Soil resources can be examined in terms of capability for agricultural productivity. This involves studying soil conditions together with climatic and relief factors to evaluate the limits that are imposed on agricultural production. It is then possible to cultivate the most suitable crop which will 1) produce an economic return and 2) not cause soil damage. Soil management – drainage, structure control, fertilizer application and irrigation – together with crop trials, can all improve soil productivity and so help to make the fullest use of a soil.

6

Soil description

6.1 Introduction

Detailed soil work usually involves making a *soil profile description*. This involves describing as many visible and tactile ('feelable') characteristics of the various horizons as is reasonably possible.

It is important to stress that it is not always necessary to make full detailed profile descriptions. Some problems require that only one or a few characteristics are noted or measured. However, in more remote areas it often makes sense to make as complete a description as possible. (It is often impossible to go back later and look again!) Section 7.10 is a discussion of the ways in which one decides precisely how much field work is really necessary.

6.2 Digging the pit

Examination of a soil is not just a matter of digging a hole and looking at it. First, it is important to stress that permission must be sought and gained before starting to dig a pit. *Every piece of land is owned by someone.* To find out who owns land ask at the nearest village or farm. If they don't own the land they'll probably be able to say who does. If you explain to the owner what you want to do, why you want to do it, and take full responsibility to be tidy and careful, most owners are very co-operative. It is also worth remembering that if one individual soil observer causes difficulties he will make problems for any who follow.

In the field you will need a strong sharp spade. (A small light spade is often easier to use than a large heavy one.) In addition a short-handled pick, a geological hammer and two plastic sheets (approximately $2\,m^2$) are useful. A penknife or small trowel can also be used for clearing up the soil face for final examination.

Having obtained permission, choose your site carefully (providing you are not following a pre-determined sampling pattern – see section 7.10). Look critically at any bumps and hollows on the landscape and avoid them. Otherwise you may find that you are making an archaeological investigation of an old road or old barn foundations. It

is also best to try and get at least twenty metres or so away from paths or field boundaries (hedges, walls, fences): these too may be the cause of soil disturbance. Remember that as far as possible one is concerned to find natural soils, undisturbed except for normal agricultural cultivations. In developed countries woodlands may have more atypical soil than agricultural land. Small woodlands are often in position because they cover old quarries or land either too bad or too difficult to farm.

Pits should be about 1 metre square. Place the plastic sheets adjacent to the chosen site, carefully remove the turves or, if in arable land, the topsoil, and place on one of the sheets. Drag the sheet away from the edge of the pit and leave on one side. Next dig out the pit to a depth of one metre, or until you reach solid rock, whichever is the shallower, placing the soil on the other sheet. When the pit is complete drag this sheet away also. It is not necessary to dig the pit to a uniform depth but only to excavate to full depth the side which one wishes to examine. When choosing which side of the pit to describe it is best to choose the side that gets most light. This will both aid description and make for easier photography, should the latter be desired.

When examination of the pit is complete drag the two plastic sheets back to the pit side. Tip in the subsoil and tamp it well down. Then replace the topsoil and turves. If the soil is very clayey and strongly structured it may be difficult to get all the soil back into the pit. In this case it is best to leave a small grave-like mound over the pit because the soil will settle in a few days. If the pit is in a field frequented by farm animals (for example, dairy pasture), it is best to cover the replaced turves with cowpats or other animal dung. Cows are very inquisitive animals and will otherwise virtually re-excavate the pit! If reasonable care is taken during excavation and examination there should be very little evidence of your efforts after work has been completed.

6.3 Site location

Before beginning to describe the soil it is important to make an accurate record of the location. In areas where large scale (1:10,000 or 1:25,000 scale) maps are available the location can be recorded by noting the grid reference. In addition make a mark on the map at the correct location and give the soil pit a number.

Where there are no large scale maps, aerial photographs are often used to give the location. In this case, there is, of course, no grid reference, but it is important to mark the photograph (or a transparent overlay) and, again, to number the soil pit.

6.4 Site description

As important as the location is a description of the site. The main features to be recorded are listed in Table 1. Depending on the purpose of the study, more detailed information on certain aspects may be required. Thus, for example, if one was studying the relationship of soil type to geomorphological features, one would want to record more about 'relief'. (A longer discussion of the different aspects of site description is given by Hodgson (1978) and, for Great Britain in Hodgson (1976).)

6.5 Soil horizons

How to recognize a horizon

As far as the soil observer is concerned a horizon is a layer of soil which differs in some way from the soil immediately above or below. It may differ simply in one property or it may differ in several; it may differ a great deal or it may differ only slightly; the difference may be only gradual and ill-defined or it may be sharp and distinct.

Nevertheless soil does not usually lie on the underlying rock in a random way, and the processes going on in the soil serve to sort it into distinct layers. Even on tip-heaps that have been recently reclaimed by artificial means incipient horizons can usually be seen. In these cases the processes have already begun to separate the individual horizons and produce a characteristic *soil profile* or combination of horizons (see section 1.1).

Soil horizons may be distinguished, for example, on the basis of colour, texture, stoniness, number of roots, soil structure and presence (or absence) of particular chemicals. Horizons are usually distinguished on the basis of features that are distinguishable *in the field*, rather than in the laboratory. (These features are sometimes known as *field*

Table 1 Items to be recorded in site description

Item	Source of information	Example
Elevation (metres)	Ordnance Survey map	35 m
Slope and aspect	Use of level or by eye	2° SE
Relief	Use of the following terms: convex concave plateau with a verbal description	Very slightly convex slope
Drainage of site	Use of the following terms: receiving (i.e. net inflow) normal shedding (i.e. net outflow) fresh-water flooding (e.g. streamside site)	Normal
Parent material	Examination at site and reference to geological literature	Shelly oolitic limestone (Chipping Norton limestone)
Vegetation or system of agriculture	Examination (in the case of natural vegetation the dominant plant species should be named)	Short ley (rye grass)
Weather		Fine; sunny after short heavy shower

characteristics.) Thus, whilst the presence or absence of carbonates might be a useful criterion, quantitative amounts (for example, above or below 0·2 ppm) would not, the calculation of quantity of carbonates requiring laboratory equipment. Equally, whilst presence of carbonates might be a useful criterion, distinction between calcium or magnesium carbonate would not. The former can be distinguished using a bottle of dilute hydrochloric acid, but the latter can best be distinguished by laboratory technique.

Fortunately for the observer, visible (or tactile, in the case of soil texture) changes usually correspond with particular chemical variations. The reason for this is quite clear. Features like colour depend on the chemical constitution, whilst features like texture and structure often control the chemical processes.

Horizon terminology

As we shall see in Chapter seven recent classifications of soil types often depend considerably on horizon classification. Some soil classifications use *diagnostic horizons* to determine ('diagnose') which group a soil belongs to. Thus it is very important that horizons themselves are correctly interpreted. It might seem that this would be a relatively easy task. However, over the years systems of horizon classification have grown up which not only describe the horizon but also contain an implicit statement about its properties: defining horizons in such a way clearly calls for some skill. (Details of horizon formation have been given in section 3.1.)

The most commonly used horizon nomenclature system has three basic units, A, B and C, which are used thus:

A Mixed mineral–organic horizon at or near the surface. This is generally a horizon of eluviation which may lose both soluble salts by drainage and also fine particles of insoluble material by mechanical downwash.
The A horizon contains a high proportion of organic material, but this is fully incorporated in the soil. Where there are thick organic accumulations above the A horizon these are classified separately.

B This is a subsurface horizon of accumulation. Essentially it is a horizon of illuviation, accumulating both mechanically downwashed material from the A horizon and also chemical depositions.

C This is the mineral matter of geological origin in which the soil horizons are forming, otherwise known as a 'parent material' horizon.

Although soils with simply these three horizons are not uncommon, there are a wide range of other possibilities. One situation is where the soil is so shallow that no distinguishable horizons are recognizable and the soil profile is simply one 'A/C horizon'. This situation is typical of calcareous rendzinas and other skeletal soils (see chapter seven).

Other letters which are used to denote particular horizons are as follows:

SURFACE HORIZONS

L fresh litter, deposited in the previous annual cycle
F partially decomposed litter from previous years (equivalent to fermentation)
H well-decomposed humus from previous years. The plant structures cannot be seen.
A see above
   Ah very dark coloured (humic) horizon often, but not necessarily, associated with high organic matter content.
   Ap ploughed layer of cultivated soils
O Peaty (organic) horizons accumulated under wet conditions

SUBSURFACE HORIZONS

Note: Where two possible alternatives are in common use the recommended method is given first and the other method second.

E eluvial mineral horizon from which clay and or sesquioxides have been removed
   Ea bleached (albic or ash-like) eluvial horizon in podzolised soils
   Eb brown (paler when dry), friable, weak-structured eluvial horizon depleted of clay
B see above; illuvial concentrations of the following materials may be denoted by suffixes thus:

   Bf, Bfe or Bi illuviated iron (chemical abbreviation: Fe), characteristic of podzols in temperate zones. (Bfe now reserved for an iron pan which looks like a sheet of rusty steel).
   Bh illuviated humus, characteristic of podzols in temperate zones
   Bm chemically weathered horizon enriched only with water-soluble salts
   Bs brightly coloured horizon containing sufficient accumulations of sesquioxide (iron and aluminium oxides in amorphous forms) arising from downward translocation, and/or alteration of silicate minerals *in situ*

Bt   illuvial clay (textural B horizon)

Bw shows evidence of alteration but does not qualify as Bf, Bh, Bs or Bt

C see above

Cu unconsolidated, ungleyed horizon

Cr weakly consolidated (includes soft rocks, e.g. siltstone)

R bedrock, which can be massive stratified or fragmented *in situ*, may have much displacement of the fragments

The following qualifying suffixes are also used:

c or ca horizons with significant amounts of calcium carbonate; c′ is used where common or abundant secondary carbonate concretions are present

cs horizon with significant amount of calcium sulphate

g gleyed horizon with greyish and/or ochreous mottling due to periodic waterlogging

(g) slightly gleyed horizon

x fragipan

A/C or AC | horizons of transitional or inter-
B/C or BC | mediate character

Lithological discontinuities in stratified parent materials (e.g., glacial drift) are given by numbered prefixes (e.g. 2B, 2C, 3C, etc.). 1 is always understood and not stated. Any minor changes between horizons which can be observed and recorded are denoted by numbered suffixes (e.g. Bg1, Bg2 or, alternatively, B1g, B2g, etc.).

(The system described here broadly follows that of the U.K. Soil Survey, although there is some simplification and, also, some additions to make it appropriate to other parts of the world.)

Examples of horizon nomenclature in use

Examples follow in which the standard horizon nomenclature has been applied to actual soil profiles. Full profile descriptions are not given yet, but come after the explanation of classification in Chapter seven.

EXAMPLE ONE

Gleyed brown earth (non-calcareous pelosol) from Gloucestershire, England, developed in calcareous drift lying over Lias clay. *Holdenby* series described by Courtney and Findlay (1978).

Horizon	Explanation of nomenclature	
A(g)	Slightly gleyed 'A'	In parent material '1' (understood)
B		
BCg	'B' intermediate to 'C', gleyed	
2Cgc	Gleyed, calcareous 'C'	In parent material '2'
3Cgc	Gleyed, calcareous 'C'	In parent material '3'

EXAMPLE TWO

Podzol developed in drift over Carboniferous Limestone, from Mendip Hills, Somerset, England. *Priddy* series described by Findlay, (1965).

Horizon	Explanation of nomenclature
A	
Ea	Bleached eluvial horizon
Bfe	Illuviated iron horizon ('iron-pan')
Eb	Brown eluvial horizon
Bt	Illuviated clayey horizon ('textural "B"')
B/C	'B' intermediate to 'C' (in this particular case the horizon is clay over limestone)

EXAMPLE THREE

Ferrisol from Sao Paulo, Brazil developed over basalt. Described by Young (1967) and FAO (1971).

Horizon	Explanation of nomenclature	
Ap	Cultivated 'A'	Distinguished by structure and consistence
B1	Upper 'B'	
B2	Middle 'B'	
B3	Lower 'B'	
BC	'B' intermediate to 'C'	

Humic gley developed in rivurine alluvium from Devon, England. *Laployd* series described by Clayden, 1971.

Horizon	Explanation of nomenclature	
L	Undecomposed litter	
F	Partially decomposed litter	
H	Well-decomposed litter (in this particular case, black amorphous peat)	
Ag	Gleyed 'A'	
C1g	Upper gleyed parent material horizon	Distinguished by amount
C2g	Middle gleyed parent material horizon	of grit, colour and
C3g	Lower gleyed parent material horizon	other features

6.6 The soil profile

The *soil profile* is the section of soil exposed either in a soil pit or in a roadside or quarry section. It extends from the ground surface down to the parent material in which the soil is developed. As has already been observed, not every soil characteristic need be noted at every soil profile examined: the number and nature of recordings depend on the project being carried out. (More discussion on this point is given in Chapter seven). If a full profile description is to be made the following features need to be noted:

depth of each horizon;

for each horizon:
    colour
    texture
    carbonates, proportion
    stoniness
    structure
    consistence
    porosity
    secondary minerals
    roots
    soil animals
    nature of lower boundary of horizon.

The description of these various characteristics will now be discussed in more detail.

Horizon depth is measured to the nearest whole centimetre. Zero is given as the top of the A horizon (or Ap, Ah or Ag horizon if appropriate). Horizons *above* the A horizon are measured using the surface of the A horizon as a baseline, whilst horizons *below*

also use the A horizon surface as zero. The following example should clarify the procedure:

Depth (cm)	Horizon
10–7	L
7–5	F
5–0	H
0–8 ------ zero ------	A
8–35	B
35+	C

Colour is noted using the Munsell soil colour system, in the form of both a written description and a numeric code. The Munsell colour system was developed in the USA and is designed to enable the coding of all possible colours (not only those found in soils). It is based on a three-dimensional colour solid (Figure 109), the axes of which represent hue, value and chroma respectively. *Hue* is the dominant spectral colour (e.g. red, yellow-red, etc.), and is related to the wavelength of light. Each dominant colour is subdivided four times. So, for example, 2·5Y, 5Y, 7·5Y, 10Y are increasing hues of yellow. *Value* is the apparent lightness or darkness and ranges from 0 (white) to 10 (black). *Chroma* refers to the purity or saturation of the colour or, in other words, the departure from the neutral greys and whites.

Soil colour is checked by reference to a soil-colour book. These contain carefully matched colour chips, the best known being the Munsell Soil Colour Charts and the Fujihira Soil Colour Charts. To check the colour the soil is first moistened to saturation (dry soil often shows different colours from wet soil), and the soil matched as nearly as possible to a colour in the book. The name and number of the colour is then noted, as in the following examples:

light reddish brown (5YR 6/4)
very dark greyish brown (2·5Y 3/2)
dark greenish grey (5G 4/1).

Both the colour of the general soil *matrix* (background) and of any *mottles* need to be noted separately, as do any additional colours in the horizon, such as those in old worm-channels. Mottles are described according to the following three scales:

Amount	Contrast	Size
abundant	prominent	coarse
common	distinct	medium
few	faint	fine
		very fine

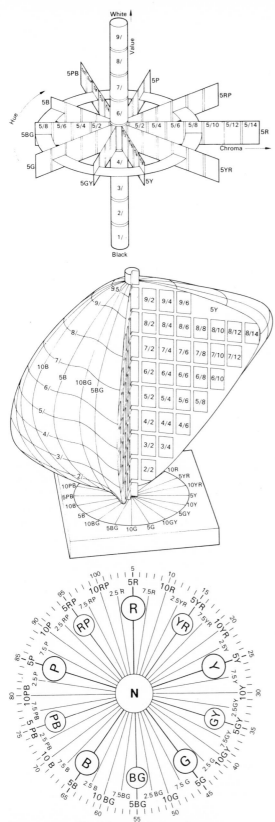

Examples of colour descriptions for mottled soils are:

grey (5Y 6/1–5/1) clay with abundant prominent coarse mottles of strong brown (7·5YR 5/6)
light olive brown (2·5Y 5/6 calcareous clay with few distinct fine mottles of greenish grey (5GY 6/1).

Where there is no definable dominant colour but many mottles the soil is described as *variegated* or *varicoloured*, thus:

Varicoloured reddish brown (5YR 5/4 and 5/3), strong brown (7·5YR 5/6 and 5/8) and yellowish red (5YR 4/6 and 5/6).

Soil texture (mineral particle size distribution: see section 2.3) is estimated using the procedure of 'hand-texturing'. This involves placing the soil in its correct particle size class (Figure 110), using the tactile characteristics of the three main particle size components – sand, silt and clay. (Full details of the size ranges and laboratory techniques are given in section 2.3.). The properties of the main grades are as follows:

'COARSE SAND consists of grains large enough to grate against each other, and can be detected individually both by feel and sight.
FINE SAND consists of grains which are far less obvious, but can still be detected, although individual grains are not easily distinguished by either feel or sight.
SILT. Individual grains cannot be detected but silt feels characteristically smooth and soapy, and only very slightly sticky.
CLAY is characteristically sticky, although some dry clays require a great deal of moistening and working between the fingers before they develop their maximum stickiness.'

(after G R Clarke, 1971)

The texture is assessed by rubbing and working a moist sample between thumb and forefinger. It is usually best to use the left hand, thus leaving the right hand free and clean for making notes (or vice versa if left-handed). Accurate texture assessment is inevitably a matter of experience, but it is surprising how quickly one can master the basic groups and knowledge of the others soon follows. It is important to remember that one is only trying to place the soil in a broad group and not accurately determine the proportions of clay, sand and silt.

The soil texture check list (Table 2) can be used as a guide to allocating an individual sample to a soil texture class.

Organic matter and chalk (or other forms of

Figure 110 The Munsell Colour System

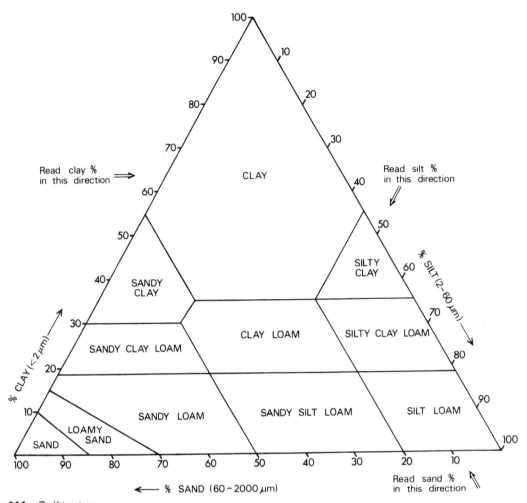

Figure 111 Soil texture

Table 2 Checklist of soil textures for moist soils

	Gritty	Soapy	Sticky	Forms Thread	Forms Ring	Takes Polish	Resistant
Sand	Very	No	No	No	No	No	No
Loamy sand	Very	No	(No)	No	No	No	No
Sandy Loam	Very	No	(No)	(Yes)	No	No	(Yes)
Sandy Clay Loam	Yes	No	Yes	Yes	(No)	Yes	Yes
Sandy Silt Loam	Yes	Yes	No	Yes	No	No	(Yes)
Silt Loam	Yes	Yes	No	(Yes)	No	No	(Yes)
Silty Clay Loam	(Yes)	Yes	Yes	Yes	(No)	Yes	Yes
Clay Loam	(Yes)	(No)	Yes	Yes	(No)	Yes	Yes
Sandy Clay	Yes	No	Yes	Yes	No	Yes	Yes
Silty Clay	No	Yes	Yes	Yes	Yes	Yes	Yes
Clay	No	No	Very	Yes	Yes	Yes	Very

( ) = weakly developed characteristic

96

finely divided calcium carbonate) tend to make the soil feel more silty and it is worth taking account of this when estimating the texture of soils containing high proportions of either.

If there is more than 15 per cent organic carbon the horizon is *humose* and the mineral texture scale is not employed. A separate scale is used as shown in the following table. (Although it is in fact percentage organic matter that is estimated in the field the table is arranged to show equivalent loss on ignition per cent.)

Descriptive term	Organic carbon (%)	Organic matter (%)	Equivalent loss on ignition (%)
Peat	>25	>43	>50
Peaty soil	15–25	26–43	30–50
Humose mineral soil	7·5–15	13–26	15–30

After Cope, 1973

Carbonates are estimated in the field by adding 10 per cent (dilute) hydrochloric acid – which can be carried in a small plastic bottle – and observing the degree of effervescence. If the soil visibly effervesces it contains more than 1% carbonates.

Stoniness is estimated visually by volume. The following CLASS descriptions are used:

Percentage	Descriptive term by volume
<1	Stoneless
1–5	Very slightly stony
6–15	Slightly stony
16–35	Moderately stony
36–70	Very stony
>70	Extremely stony

SIZE of stones is estimated as follows:

Size (diameter, mm)	Descriptive term
2–6	Very small stones
6–20	Small stones
20–60	Medium stones
60–200	Large stones
200–600	Very large stones
600	Boulders

SHAPE of stones is noted using the following terms:

rounded (including nodular formations)
sub-rounded (including nodular formations)
angular (including cubic and flat varieties)
sub-angular (including cubic and flat varieties)
Terms such as shaly, flaggy, etc. which imply lithology should not be used to describe shape. Stones with unequal axes should be described further as tabular or platy.

KIND of stones i.e. lithology (e.g. granite, limstone, shale).

An example of a stoniness description is: 'stony with small to medium angular and subangular cherts'.

Structure. DEGREE of structure development is noted using the following scale:

STRUCTURELESS. No observable peds; massive if coherent and single-grain if non-coherent.
WEAK. Indistinct peds; when disturbed the soil breaks into much aggregated material.
MODERATE. Well-formed peds; little unaggregated soil when disturbed.
STRONG. Peds distinct in place; soil remains aggregated when disturbed.

SHAPE of peds is noted as follows:

PLATY. Vertical axis much shorter than horizontal.
PRISMATIC. Vertical axis longer than horizontal, vertical faces well defined, vertices usually angular.
COLUMNAR. Prisms with rounded tops.
BLOCKY. Peds roughly equidimensional, and enclosed by plane or curved surfaces that are casts or moulds formed by faces of adjacent peds; subdivided into angular (sharp edges) and subangular.
GRANULAR. Small, subrounded or irregular peds without distinct edges or faces, usually hard and relatively non-porous.
CRUMB. Soft, porous, granular aggregates like bread crumbs.

Each shape of peds is divided into *size* classes as shown in the following table:

Ped type	Size description (ped diameter, mm)				
	Very fine	Fine	Medium	Coarse	Very coarse
Platy	<1	1–2	2–5	5–10	>10
Prismatic/ columnar	<10	10–20	20–50	50–100	>100
Blocky	<5	5–10	10–20	20–50	>50
Granular	<1	1–2	2–5	5–10	>10
Crumb	<1	1–2	2–5	n.a.	n.a.

n.a. = not applicable.

Consistence is the term used to describe the degree and kind of cohesion of soil material or fragments and varies with moisture content. The descriptive term applied refers to the moistness when sampled:

LOOSE. Non-coherent when moist or dry.

FRIABLE. Moist soil crumbles under gentle pressure to fairly uniform aggregates which cohere slightly when pressed together; the term *'labile'* indicates stronger cohesion after crumbling.

FIRM. Moist soil crushes under moderate to strong pressure but offers distinct resistance; *very firm* soil material is difficult to crush between finger and thumb.

HARD. Dry soil is moderately resistant to pressure; it can be broken in the hands, but is barely breakable between thumb and fingers; *very hard* soil material can be broken in the hand only with difficulty.

BRITTLE. Material resists deformation and breaks suddenly under pressure.

PLASTIC. Very moist or very wet soil can be moulded and rolled into shapes without breaking.

STICKY. Very moist or wet soil adheres to the hands.

SOFT. Soil yields easily under pressure.

Porosity gives an approximate indication of the quantity and size of fissures and pores in the soil. The following terms are usually used to describe porosity, although it should be remembered that porosity is to some extent a reflection of moisture conditions at the time of description:

FREQUENCY	SIZE
abundant	coarse
common	medium
few	fine

Secondary minerals are described by abundance, form and size. They may include secondary carbonate, manganiferous and gypseous deposits. Examples of descriptions are:

few medium and coarse secondary manganiferous deposits
common fine secondary carbonate concretions.

Roots. The following method of describing roots is in common usage. QUANTITY is noted per $30\,cm^2$ of profile face:

Abundant	more than 100
Frequent	100–20
Few	20–4
Rare	3–1

SIZE is noted as follows:

Large	more than 1 cm diameter
Medium	1 cm–3 mm
Small	3–1 mm
Fine	less than 1 mm

TYPE of root is noted as either:

woody,
fleshy,
fibrous or
rhizomatous

An example of root description is: 'abundant small fibrous roots'.

Soil animals are recorded in a brief verbal description, e.g. type and abundance.

Horizon boundaries. At the end of each horizon description a note is made of the nature of the lower horizon boundary. The following terms are usually used in the description. SHAPE of the boundary is described as:

EVEN: when the horizon is at the same depth across the whole of the visible profile.

UNDULATING: when upward and downward projections are wider than their depth.

IRREGULAR: when projections are deeper than their width.

CLARITY of the boundary is described as:

SHARP: when the transition zone is less than 2 cm thick.

NARROW: when the transition zone is 2–5 cm thick.

MERGING: when the transition zone is greater than 5 cm thick.

Examples of soil profile descriptions are given in the following Chapter. One final point is worth remembering when making a soil profile description. It is far better to write down exactly what you see than to avoid doing so simply because you have no appropriate term or phrase available – even if this means a lengthy and wordy description. Once the pit has been filled in you cannot have another look!

6.7 Example profile descriptions

Seven example soil-profile descriptions are now given. The first four examples are from Great Britain (which has a temperate climate) and are taken from Soil Survey Memoirs (see section 7.6). The remainder of the examples are from tropical areas.

The profile descriptions are given to show how full soil profile descriptions should be laid out: in general the descriptions accord with the terminology outlined in sections 6.5 and 6.6, although some variations will be noticed, particularly in soil texture nomenclature.

Profile 1   Lithomorphic soil: rendzina
(after Jarvis, 1973)

GRID REFERENCE SU 285827
LOCATION Ashdown Farm, Ashbury, Berks.
RELIEF steep convex valley side
SLOPE AND ELEVATION 10°WSW, 220 m OD
LAND USE permanent downland grassland
HORIZONS

cm

0–13 A	Very dark greyish-brown (10YR 3/2), very friable, very calcareous, slightly stony (medium angular flints) humose silty clay loam; strong fine and very fine crumb structure; extremely abundant fine fibrous roots; many clusters of faecal pellets; narrow even boundary.
13–44 AC	Dark greyish-brown (10YR 4/2), very friable, very calcareous silt loam with stones dominant, gravel to medium brown-stained subangular chalk and common medium to large angular and broken flints; in larger patches of matrix, strong fine crumb or subangular blocky structure; clusters of faecal pellets; abundant fine fibrous roots between stones; merging boundary.
44 + C	Broken brown-stained Upper Chalk (Chalk Rock) *in situ*.

Profile 2   Brown soil: brown earth (sensu stricto)
(after Clayden, 1971)

GRID REFERENCE SX 803699
LOCATION Wotten Cross, Denbury, Devon
ELEVATION 100 m OD   SLOPE AND ASPECT 2°S
LAND USE Ley grass
HORIZONS

cm

0–20 Ap	Dark brown (7·5YR–10YR 4/2) clay loam; stony throughout with predominantly fine slate fragments and occasional small stones of limestone,

vesicular lava and dolerite; moderate, very fine subangular blocky structure; friable; moderate organic matter; abundant fine roots; merging boundary.

20–46 B1	Brown (10YR–7·5YR 4/3) loam; moderate to fine strong crumb structure; extremely friable; moderate organic matter; roots common; merging boundary.
46–58 B2	Brown to yellowish-brown (10YR 4/5–3/5) loam; weak fine crumb structure; friable; few roots; narrow boundary.
58–81 + C	*In situ* slate with very fine laminae, easily broken.

Profile 3   Podzolic soil
(after Clayden, 1971)

GRID REFERENCE SX 797749
LOCATION Rora Wood, Liverton, Devon
ELEVATION 120 m OD   SLOPE AND ASPECT 20°NW
LAND USE oak coppice with heathy ground vegetation
HORIZONS

cm

10–0 H	Dark brown (5YR 2/2) amorphous organic matter; very fine crumb structure; abundant woody and fibrous roots, particularly concentrated above boundary to Ea horizon; narrow boundary.
0–56 Ea	Light grey (10YR 6/1, dry) sandy loam, with greyish-brown (10YR 5/2) patches in lower part of horizon; stone dominant, mainly gravel and small angular chert; structureless; loose; low organic matter; common fine fibrous roots; narrow irregular boundary.
56–58 B1h	Dark reddish-brown (5YR 3/2) loam with some areas of 5YR 2/2 and variegated with greyish brown and strong brown; extremely stony; structureless, massive; firm, weakly indurated; high organic matter; narrow irregular boundary.
58–96 B2s	Strong brown (7·5YR 5/8) loam, becoming of yellower hue with depth, with occasional coarse pockets of

reddish-brown humus staining; extremely stony, small to medium angular cherts; weak fine crumb structure; friable; moderate organic matter; few roots; merging boundary.

96–124
BC
Yellowish-brown (10YR 5/6) loam with some humus staining; otherwise as above; merging boundary.

124–183+
C
Very pale brown (10YR 7/3) loam; extremely stony, mainly gravel to small stones, some soft and partially weathered (but not cheesy) chert; weak fine angular blocky structure; crumbles readily; few roots.

Profile 4   Gley soil
(after Jarvis, 1973)

GRID REFERENCE SP 318003
LOCATION Carswell Marsh, Buckland, Oxon
RELIEF Thames floodplain
SLOPE AND ELEVATION level; 65 m OD
LAND USE permanent grass
HORIZONS

cm

0–12
Ag
Very dark grey (10 YR 3/1) humose, friable, stoneless calcareous clay with ochreous staining along 50 per cent of roots; moderate fine crumb structure; extremely fine abundant fibrous roots; many small gastropod shells; narrow boundary.

12–20
Bg
Greyish-brown (10YR 5/2), reddish-yellow (7·5YR 6/8) mottled, slightly humose, friable, very calcareous clay; moderate, breaking to fine, subangular blocky structure; common fine pores; abundant fine fibrous roots; a few small concretions at centre of yellowish-red (5YR 4/8) mottles; many small gastropod shells; merging boundary.

20–37
Cgca
Light brownish-grey (2·5Y 6/2), yellowish-red (7·5YR 6/6) mottled, sticky massive stoneless, very calcareous clay; common fine fibrous roots; a few small gastropod shells; a few secondary CaCO$_3$ concretions and secondary CaCO$_3$ also infilling many pores; narrow boundary.

37–50
2Cg1
Grey (N5/0), with large reddish-yellow (7·5YR 6/6) mottles, sticky massive stoneless clay; common fine pores; common dead fine fibrous roots; merging boundary.

50–90
2Cg2
Grey to light grey (N6/0), with large reddish-yellow (7·5YR 6/8) mottles, sticky massive calcareous clay; common fine pores and dead, fine fibrous roots; small ferruginous concretions at centre of some mottles.

Profile 5   Leached ferrallitic soil
(after Young, 1979)

LOCATION Jengka Triangle, Pahang State, West Malaysia; 4°N, 102°E.
ELEVATION 100m   SLOPE 6°
LAND USE Lowland evergreen rainforest
CLIMATE Rainforest type with no dry season.
HORIZONS

cm

0–8
Ah
Yellowish brown (10YR5/4) sandy loam; moderate medium crumb structure; almost loose consistence; many roots; clear boundary.

8–45
A2
Brownish yellow (10YR6/6) sandy clay loam; weak medium blocky structure, no clay skins; very friable; roots common; merging boundary.

45–110
Bt
Brownish yellow (10YR6/6) sandy clay loam; moderate medium blocky structure; friable; few roots merging boundary.

110–280
BC
Strong brown (7.5YR5/6) sandy clay loam; moderate medium angular blocky structure; firm few roots; mottle from weathered rock increasing towards base.

Profile 6   Ferrisol
(after Young, 1979 from FAO-Unesco, 1971)

LOCATION Sao Paulo State, Brazil; 23°S, 50°W.
ELEVATION 580m   SLOPE 3°
LAND USE Coffee plantation; formerly semi-deciduous forest.
CLIMATE Humid subtropical
HORIZONS

cm

0–19
Ap
Dark reddish brown (2.5YR3/4) clay; strong fine and medium blocky structure; very firm, plastic; abundant roots; clear boundary.

19–80
B1
Dark reddish brown (2.5YR3/4) clay; strong fine and medium blocky structure; firm, plastic; clear boundary.

80–134
B2
Dark reddish brown (2.5YR 3/4) clay; moderate fine blocky structure; soft, friable, slightly plastic; few roots merging boundary.

134–224
B3
Dark reddish brown (2.5YR 3/4) clay; massive, breaking into weak fine granular structure; soft, very friable; no roots; merging, wavy boundary.

224–250 Dark brown (7.5YR 5/6) clay; soft, very
friable.

Profile 7   Vertisol
(after Young 1979)

LOCATION Shemankar Valley, Benue Plateau
State, Nigeria; 9°E, 9°N.
ELEVATION 400m   SLOPE ½°
LAND USE Grassland. Mainly used for nomadic
grazing; small patches cultivated successfully for
rice and less so for sorghum.
CLIMATE Moist savanna.
HORIZONS

cm
0–10 Ah	Dark greyish brown (10YR 4/2) clay; strong fine blocky structure; plastic, very sticky; many grass roots; clear boundary.
10–45 Bg1	Greyish brown (10YR 5/2) with ped surface grey, heavy clay; strong fine and medium angular blocky structure; plastic, very stiff, very sticky; roots common, merging boundary.
45–150 Bg2	Dark greyish brown (2.5Y 4/2) with ped surfaces slightly greyer, heavy clay; strong course prismatic plus moderate to strong medium angular blocky structure; plastic, very stiff, very sticky; occasional $CaCO_3$ concretions; very few roots.

7

Soil classification

7.1 Introduction

The essential aim of this chapter is to enable the reader to understand the purpose and application of soil classification – particularly as it relates to soil maps. Soil classification can be a notoriously complicated subject: part of the reason for this is the large number of different schemes that have been used (and in many cases still are being used) throughout the world. This chapter is, therefore, an introduction and the reader is referred to the section on Further Reading (p.118) for more advanced texts on the subject.

7.2 Why classify?

One purpose of soil classification is to enable generalized information to be easily transmitted from one individual to another. If there were no form of classification at all it would be necessary to give a full profile description every time one referred to a particular profile. For many (indeed most) purposes this is more than is required and a simple summary word or phrase is all that is needed. This gives the individual receiving the information a basic idea of the main features and saves a great deal of time.

A second purpose of soil classification is in *theory construction*. The advancement of any science depends upon being able to make generalizations and predictive statements about what will happen in particular circumstances. To enable this development to take place in soil science it is clearly necessary to combine soils in groups (or classify soils) in such a way that all members of any particular group respond in similar ways and are thus able to have predictive statements made about them. For example, for agricultural purposes it is obviously helpful if one can make predictive statements about how a group of soils respond to particular fertilizers. (We will refer to some of the problems of theory constructions with soils in section 7.7.)

To enable these two long-term aims to be achieved, the short-term objective of soil classifica-

tion is that soils must be grouped in such a way that each group has a minimum of diversity *within* it and a maximum of diversity *between* groups.

7.3 The basic unit of classification

In plant and animal classifications, organisms fall into easily recognizable classificatory units – the species. Each species can be fairly clearly defined and it is only in unusual circumstances that species interbreed to produce intergrades. In the case of soil, however, the choice of a suitable basic classificatory unit is more difficult. One has only to look at a soil profile to see that there is a considerable range of variation laterally across the profile (ignoring the obvious vertical horizon variation). It is therefore necessary to state some artificial limits to the chosen basic unit. In many classifications the basic unit is the *soil profile,* which is:

'considered for the purpose as three-dimensional, with lateral dimensions large enough to evaluate diagnostic properties of horizons at a particular place.'

B W Avery, 1973, p. 325

Effectively one is defining the soil profile as having no lateral variation. In the United States a different unit – the *soil pedon* – is employed. This is an artificially defined three-dimensional cuboid having lateral dimensions which depend on the lateral variability of the properties of the defined class.

7.4 Development of soil classification

The first significant attempts at soil classification were those of the Russian school – led by Dokuchaiev – which were published in the 1880s. The Russian classification was based on the assumption that soil type was largely determined by climate, and this is, of course, generally true for the large-scale soil belts with which the Russians were concerned. This kind of classification is known as a *typological* classification.

The basis of Dokuchaiev's classification was as follows:

Zone   *Soil Type*

CLASS A: NORMAL, OTHERWISE DRY LAND VEGETATIVE OR ZONAL SOILS

1. Boreal — Tundra (dark brown) soils
2. Taiga — Light grey podzolised soils
3. Forest-steppe — Grey and dark grey soils
4. Steppe — Chernozem
5. Desert-steppe — Chestnut and brown soils
6. Aerial or desert-zone — Aerial soils, yellow soils, white soils
7. Sub-tropical and zone of tropical forests — Laterite or red soils

CLASS B: TRANSITIONAL SOILS

8. Dry land moor soils or moor-meadow soils
9. Carbonate-containing soils (rendzina)
10. Secondary alkaline soils

CLASS C: ABNORMAL SOILS

11. Moor soils
12. Alluvial soils
13. Aeolian soils

Development of typological classifications took place throughout the first fifty years of this century, different versions being produced for various parts of the world. However, whilst the general premise that climate is the main determinant of soil distribution holds true on a large continental scale, it becomes increasingly difficult to apply at smaller scales. Other factors begin to over-ride climate in their importance (see section 3.1), and it becomes more and more difficult to interrelate the factors and therefore to complete the soil classification. Much more research is needed before we are fully aware of the relative importance of the factors responsible for soil formation and variation.

The realization of this complexity has led to the replacement of typological classifications by *definitional* classifications, the first of these which entered common use being that of the United States Department of Agriculture (USDA). (See section 7.7.) Definitional classifications depend on a description of the soil. The soils most alike are grouped together, trying to make little or no implicit statement about soil genesis.

7.5 The 1940 British classification

Detailed British soil mapping commenced in the nineteen-twenties, but it was not until 1940 that enough information had been assembled to enable a detailed classification system to be generally adopted. The scheme is based on six main soil groups:

1 brown earth;
2 podzols;
3 gley soils;
4 calcareous soils;
5 organic soils and
6 undifferentiated alluvium.

These groups are basically derived from the Dokuchaiev system and relate closely to those in continental European classification produced at about the same time. Details of the groups in the classification are given in Table 3.

With some minor modifications the classification has been used until 1974 in publications of the Soil Survey of Great Britain. In recent years a new definitional classification has been developed.

7.6 The 1980 British classification

As already stated the basic unit of classification is the soil profile. The classification is, in general, based on observable *field properties* of profiles and, as far as possible, depends on those that are permanent. For example, thin surface layers easily destroyed by cultivation do not qualify as distinguishing horizons.

Table 4 lists the major groups and groups. The higher categories are distinguished by combinations of the two main factors:

1 the composition of the soil within specified depth limits, and
2 presence or absence of diagnostic horizons generally reflecting degree or kind of alteration of the original material.

It can be seen that the second factor contains an implicit statement about soil genesis and to this limited extent the classification is not entirely definitional. It can also be seen from the table that the major groups bear names generally similar to those in previous use. However, these are now precisely defined and it is apparent that a number of other new names have been introduced to distinguish the lower order of groups and subgroups. This was necessary because many of the old names were being applied to different types of soil by different workers in various countries.

Explanation of some of the terms used in the new classification will now be given. Details of where to find more information are given in Further Reading (p.118).

Humose mineral materials are those containing more than 4·5–7·0 per cent organic carbon.
Ferritic soils are those in which the Fe_2O_3 content is more than 4 per cent and more than half the measured clay percentage.

Distinct topsoil. A cultivated soil with an appreciably darkened Ap horizon containing at least 0·6 per cent organic carbon in the upper 15 cm, or an uncultivated soil with as much or more organic matter and continuous O or H or Ah horizons (whichever is present) together more than 7·5 cm thick.

Table 3 1940 soil classification

___

DEFINITIONS

I Soils of the brown-earth group

Three characteristics form the basic definition of the normal brown earths:

1 The soil has free drainage throughout the profile.
2 There is no vertical differentiation of silica and sesquioxides in the clay fraction.
3 There is no natural free $CaCO_3$ in the soil horizon.

Other morphological and chemical features may vary. Thus the soil may be of any colour, but this colour is more or less uniform throughout the profile; the degree of acidity may vary widely.

The virgin soils are usually characterized by an accumulation of leaf litter on the surface, which is underlain by mull humus. Under cultivation the surface is altered, added bases may be present, and to this extent arable soils will differ from the normal brown earths.

The brown-earth group is divided into soils of low base status and soils of high base status. Soils with a high base status are only slightly acid, and become neutral with depth; they are derived from base-rich parent materials. Those of low base status have a tendency to acidity throughout the profile.

Subtypes of the brown-earth group

A *Creep or colluvial soils* – This group is dependent on topography for its development. In morphological and chemical characteristics it is the same as the normal brown earth soils.
B *Brown earths with gleyed B and C horizons* – The soils of this subtype are the same as the normal brown earths except for a suggestion of gleying in the lower horizons. This gleying is no more than an occasional bluish or rusty mottling. The effect may be due to rare rises in ground water or to a slight impedance in drainage.
C *Leached soils from calcareous parent materials* – These soils are characterized by a red-brown colour and a condition of base unsaturation. They may be quite acid, and if $CaCO_3$ is present it is in the form of hard lumps. Organic matter is light in colour, but is not necessarily low. Secondary $CaCO_3$ may occur at the base of the B horizon, or in the parent material.

II Soils of the podzol group

The chief morphological characteristics of normal podzolized soils are:

1 The presence of a bleached (grey) layer under the surface raw humus.
2 The yellow to rusty coloured accumulation layer which follows.

The chemical characteristics are found in the differentiation of the silica and sesquioxides of the clay fraction. Under cultivation the surface raw humus is absent. Arable soils may show the typical grey and rusty layers, or these may be almost entirely obliterated. All transitions occur, but so long as the clay fraction shows differentiation of the silica and sesquioxides, such soils are included in the podzol group.

Subtypes of the podzol group

A *Slightly to strongly podzolized soils* – These depend on the thickness of the bleached horizon.
B *Concealed podzols* – The soil has a raw humus surface layer but no bleached layer. The translocation of sesquioxide is proved by the changes in the silica–sesquioxide ratio.
C *Peaty podzolized soils* – In these the raw humus has developed into peat. They may vary from a slightly to strongly podzolized condition (for definition of peat see later).
D *Podzolized soils with gleying* – These are essentially podzolized soils in the upper layers, but exhibit signs of impedance by gleying in the B or C horizons.
E *Truncated podzols* – Here the surface soil has the characters of a B horizon. Under grass vegetation the iron colours are washed by humus.

III Soils of the gley group

The characteristic of gleying is the presence of greenish, bluish-grey, rusty, or yellowish spots or mottling:

Table 3 *(contd)*

1 *Surface-water gley soils* – In these the excessive water is on the surface and produces gleying in the surface horizons. In the lower horizons gleying progressively decreases or may be absent altogether.

2 *Groundwater gley soils* – The surface of such soils may be dry, at least seasonally and often permanently, with little or no gleying. Gleying is essentially present in the lower layers. This group includes soils with slow percolation, not necessarily occurring only in depressions.

Subtypes of groundwater gley soils

A *Gley podzolized soils* – These soils have a raw humus surface and a bleached A horizon. The B horizon is thin or absent. Gleying occurs below this level.

B *Peaty gley podzolized soils* – Essentially similar to A but peat replaces raw humus.

C *Peaty gley soils* – These soils are completely gleyed and carry a peaty surface.

D *Gley calcareous soils* – These are characterized by a grey colour and a moderately high organic matter content. Calcium carbonate occurs throughout the profile and increases with depth; the soil is base saturated. There is little change in the silica–sesquioxide ratio down the profile. Secondary calcium carbonate often occurs in the form of concretions, especially in the lower layers. Gleying is shown by the presence of bluish, greenish, rusty, or yellow spots and mottling.

IV Soils of the calcareous group

These soils are developed from calcareous parent materials, contain primary calcium carbonate in the soil horizons, and are base saturated.

Subtypes of the calcareous group

A *Grey calcareous soils* (rendzina type) – Under natural vegetation these soils show a very dark surface horizon, a high content of organic matter, and a well-developed crumb structure. There is no differentiation of the silica–sesquioxide ratio down the profile. Calcium carbonate increases in amount with depth until the parent material is reached. Secondary deposition of calcium carbonate may occur. Under arable cultivation organic matter is lower, calcium carbonate is higher, and the soils may be pale grey or almost white in colour. Crumb structure is less pronounced.

B *Red and brown calcareous soils* – These are formed on hard limestone and do not occur on the chalk. They are shallow, being characterized by a red or brown colour and by the presence of fragmentary calcareous

rock. The organic matter content is usually low and the silica–sesquioxide ratio constant throughout the profile. Secondary deposition of calcium carbonate may occur in the parent material.

C *Calcareous soils with gleyed B and C horizons* – These soils, in the upper layers, are similar to either subtypes **A** or **B**, but show slight gleying in the lower horizons.

V Soils of the organic group

The soil character is determined by the presence of twenty or more centimetres of waterlogged organic matter, termed peat. There are two groups:

1 *Basin peat* – Soligenous in origin, i.e. formed under the influence of excessive or stagnant groundwater.

2 *Moss peat* – Ombrogenous in origin, i.e. formed under the influence of heavy rainfall and low summer temperature.

Basin peat. The main development forms of this group are as follows:

A1 *Fen* (including Carr) – This is formed under the influence of calcareous or base-rich groundwater. Transition phase is grass-moor, etc.

A2 *Raised moss* – This is ombrogenous as a result of accumulation of **A1** above groundwater level.

B1 *Acid low moor* – This is formed under the influence of drainage from acid or base-poor rock and soils, e.g. podzolized surface or raised moss.

B2 *Raised moss* – As in **A2**.

Note – Moss peats are predominantly ombrogenous since they develop under conditions of high rainfall on a substratum lying above groundwater level. The ultimate form of these is 'raised moss' and may develop over any organic soil when it grows above groundwater influence. Moss peat covering a region is termed 'blanket moss' and is to be regarded as climatic in the pedological sense.

*Subtype of **B2** – hill peat*

This is a variety of blanket moss formed on hilltops and slopes which varies from the main type in distribution and character and is therefore to be mapped separately as 'hill peat'.

VI Undifferentiated alluvium group

Owing to the great variety of soils which may be encountered in a comparatively small area of alluvium, some surveyors do not attempt to differentiate them. In such cases the soils are allocated to this group. Where alluvial flats are extensive careful survey will be worth while. In this case the different series identified will be allocated to one of the other five groups.

Source: G R Clarke, *Soil Survey of England and Wales, Field Handbook*, Oxford University Press, 1940.

Table 4 Soil classification in England and Wales source Avery, 1980)

Major group	Group
Lithomorphic (A/C) soils Normally well-drained soils with distinct, humose or organic topsoil and bedrock or little altered unconsolidated material at 30 cm or less	*Rankers* With non-calcareous topsoil over bedrock (including massive limestone) or non-calcareous unconsolidated material (excluding sand) *Sand-rankers* In non-calcareous, sandy material *Ranker-like alluvial soils* In non-calcareous recent alluvium (usually coarse textured) *Rendzinas* Over extremely calcarous non-alluvial material, fragmentary limestone or chalk *Pararendzinas* Over moderately calcareous non-alluvial (excluding sand) material *Sand-pararendzinas* In calcareous sandy material *Rendzina-like alluvial soils* In calcareous recent alluvium
Brown soils Well drained to imperfectly drained soils (excluding pelosols) with an altered subsurface (B) horizon, usually brownish, that has soil structure rather than rock structure and extends below 30 cm depth	*Brown calcareous earths* Non-alluvial, loamy or clayey, with friable moderately calcareous subsurface horizon *Brown calcareous sands* Non-alluvial, sandy with moderately calcareous subsurface horizon *Brown calcareous alluvial soils* In calcareous recent alluvium *Brown earths (sensu stricto)* Non-alluvial, non calcareous loamy, with brown or reddish friable subsurface horizon *Brown sands* Non-alluvial, sandy or sandy gravelly *Brown alluvial soils* Non-calcareous in recent alluvium *Argillic brown earths* Loamy or loamy over clayey, with subsurface horizon of clay accumulation, normally brown or reddish *Paleo-argillic brown earths* Loamy or clayey, with strong brown to red subsurface horizon of clay accumulation, attributable to pedogenic alteration before the last glacial period

Table 4   *(contd)*

Major group   *Group*

Podzolic soils
Well-drained to poorly drained soils with black,
dark brown or ochreous subsurface (B) horizon
in which aluminium and/or iron have accumulated
in amorphous forms associated with organic
matter. An overlying bleached horizon, a peaty
topsoil or both may or may not be present.

Pelosols
Slowly permeable non-alluvial clayey soils that
crack deeply in dry seasons with brown, greyish
or reddish blocky or prismatic subsurface horizon,
usually slightly mottled

Gley soils
With distinct, humose or peaty topsoil and grey or
grey-and-brown mottled (gleyed) sub-surface
horizon altered by reduction, or reduction and
segregation, of iron caused by periodic or
permanent saturation by water in the presence of
organic matter. Horizons characteristic of podzolic
soils are absent

Group

Brown podzolic soils
Loamy or sandy, normally well drained, with a dark
brown or ochreous friable subsurface horizon
and no overlying bleached horizon or peaty topsoil

Gley-podzols
With dark brown or black subsurface horizon over a
grey or mottled (gleyed) horizon affected by
fluctuating groundwater or impeded drainage. A
bleached horizon, a peaty topsoil, or both may
be present

Podzols (sensu stricto)
Sandy or coarse loamy, normally well drained, with
a bleached horizon and/or dark brown or black
subsurface horizon enriched in humus and no
immediately underlying grey or mottled (gleyed)
horizon or peaty topsoil

Stagnopodzols
With peaty topsoil, periodically wet (gleyed) bleached
horizon, both, over a thin iron-pan and/or a
brown or ochreous relatively friable subsurface
horizon

Calcareous pelosols
With calcareous subsurface horizon

Argillic pelosols
With subsurface horizon of clay accumulation,
normally non-calcareous

Non-calcareous pelosols
Without argillic horizon

1 Gley soils without a humose or peaty topsoil,
seasonally wet in the absence of effective artificial
drainage

Alluvial grey soils
In loamy or clayey recent alluvium affected by
fluctuating groundwater

Sandy gley soils
Sandy, permeable, affected by fluctuating
groundwater

Cambic gley soils
Loamy or clayey, non-alluvial, with a relatively
permeable substratum affected by fluctuating
groundwater

Argillic gley soils
Loamy or loamy over clayey, with a subsurface
horizon of clay accumulation and a relatively
permeable substratum affected by fluctuating
groundwater

Table 4 *(contd)*

Major group	*Group*
	Stagnogley soils Non-calcareous, non-alluvial, with loamy or clayey, relatively impermeable subsurface horizon or substratum that impedes drainage
	2 Gley soils with a humose or peaty topsoil, normally wet for most of the year in the absence of effective artificial drainage
	Humic-alluvial gley soils In loamy or clayey recent alluvium
	Humic-sandy gley soils Sandy, permeable, affected by high groundwater
	Humic gley soils (sensu stricto) Loamy or clayey, non-alluvial affected by high groundwater
	Stagnohumic gley soils Non-calcareous, with loamy or clayey, relatively impermeable subsurface horizon or sub-stratum that impedes drainage
Manmade soils *With thick manmade topsoil or disturbed soil (including material recognizably derived from pedogenic horizons) more than 40 cm thick*	*Manmade humic soils* With thick manmade topsoil *Disturbed soils* Without thick manmade topsoil
Peat soils With a dominantly organic layer at least 40 cm thick, formed under wet conditions and starting at the surface or within 30 cm depth	*Raw peat soils* Permanently waterlogged and/or contain more than 15 per cent recognizable plant remains within the upper 20 cm *Earthy peat soils* With relatively firm (drained) topsoil, normally black, containing few recognizable plant remains

Humose topsoil. An A horizon that is humose over at least 15 cm depth or 10–15 cm if directly over bedrock or fragmental material.

Peaty topsoil. An O horizon 7·5–40 cm thick, over a mineral subsurface horizon.

Thick manmade A horizon. A dark A horizon more than 40 cm thick resulting from addition of manure containing earth or otherwise attributable to human occupation.

Podzolic B horizon. B horizon or horizons in which organic matter and aluminium and/or iron have accumulated. It usually underlies a bleached (albic) E horizon or a dark Ah, H or O horizon and is required to extend to at least 15 cm depth, excluding surface litter. The following horizons can form all or part of a podzolic B:

Bh   normally dark coloured with little iron
Bhs dark coloured, more than 1 cm thick, with proportionately more iron
Bs   brown or ochreous
Bf (or Bfe) thin iron pan
(More details of these horizons are given in section 6.5 p. 92).

Humic and *Ferri-humic* podzols have Bhs horizons that are humose over at least 10 cm and generally lack an E horizon.

Argillic (Bt) horizon. Textural B horizon containing translocated silicate clay. It is required to contain significantly more clay than all overlying horizons.

Palaeo-argillic soils show features (e.g. reddish colours due to prolonged weathering) that were derived before the last (Weichselian) glacial period.

Weathered B (Bw) horizon. Non-podzolic, non-argillic B horizon is usually brownish and differentiated by colour and/or structural features. As a diagnostic horizon (Brown soils major group) it is required to extend at least 10 cm below an Ap horizon or to more than 30 cm depth, and extremely calcareous material is excluded. A shallower brownish weathered horizon (A/Bw) characterizes brown rankers and brown rendzinas.

Sandy soils. For inclusion in sandy groups or subgroups, at least half the upper 80 cm of mineral soil must be sand or loamy sand.

Vertic features. The soils classed as pelosols are identified by the following characteristics:

1 More than 35 per cent clay over at least 30 cm, starting at the surface, directly below the Ap, or at less than 25 cm depth.
2 Blocky, prismatic or wedge-shaped peds with glazed faces, often inclined.
3 Cracks more than 5 mm wide between 25 and 50 cm depth in most years.

Calcareous soils are those lacking an argillic horizon and have a Bw, Bg or C horizon containing at least 1 per cent $CaCO_3$ at less than 40 cm depth.

Alluvial soils comprise those in fluviatile, marine or lacustrine deposits at least 30 cm thick.

7.7   The United States 'Soil Taxonomy' (USDA 1975)

This is a widely used definitional system, drawn up by soil scientists working in the United States. In many ways it developed as a reaction to the older typological classifications. This classification comprises a hierarchy of six categorical levels with keys available to identify all classes. Thus, the intention is to have one universal system which can incorporate all possibilities. The classification of soils in this system depends on the identification of a *diagnostic horizon* (or combination of horizons) in the profile. Several soil scientists have criticised this approach on the grounds (amongst others) that it is difficult to incorporate intergrade soils in the USDA system – this, in itself, they say, is in conflict with the intrinsic nature of soil.

Ten soil orders encompass all variation. The orders and their general characteristics are:

Entisols	recently formed soils
Vertisols	shrinking and swelling clay soils
Inceptisols	soils without contrasting horizons
Aridosols	soils of arid regions
Mollisols	soils with mull humus
Spodosols	soils with iron and humus B horizons
Alfisols	soils with clay B horizons and high base status
Ultisols	soils with clay B horizons and low base status
Oxisols	sesquioxide-rich highly weathered soils (lateric soils)
Histosols	peats

7.8   The FAO Classification (FAO 1974)

The FAO (Food and Agricultural Organisation of United Nations) classification was developed for use on the world soil map and has both typological and definitional features. There are 26 basic categories arranged in a logical order according to an increasing degree of weathering and profile development. Although the classification is based on a logical soil genesis scale, diagnostic horizons broadly similar to those in the USDA schemes are used for profile identification. One difference of particular significance is the inclusion in the FAO scheme of gleyed horizons as diagnostic – gley horizons are not diagnostic in the USDA scheme.

The main soil groups are as follows:

(1) Fluvisols	alluvial and colluvial soils
(2) Gleysols	hydromorphic soils
(3) Regosols	slightly developed soils on unindurated materials
(4) Lithosols	slightly developed soils on hard rock
(5) Arenosols	soils with a sandy texture
(6) Rendzinas	
(7) Rankers	
(8) Andosols	
(9) Vertisols	
(10) Solontchaks	
(11) Solonetz	
(12) Yermosols	arid soils without organic matter
(13) Xerosols	arid soils with organic matter
(14) Kastanozems	chestnut steppe soils
(15) Chernozems	
(16) Phaeozems	brunizems and lessived chernozems
(17) Greyzems	grey forest soils
(18) Cambisols	temperate or tropical brown soils
(19) Luvisols	temperate lessived soils, lessived fersiallitic soils
(20) Podzols	
(21) Podzoluvisols	lessived soils or glossic podzolic soils
(22) Planosols	
(23) Acrisols	utisols (USDA), lessived acid ferrunginous soils
(24) Nitosols	tropical ferrisols
(25) Ferralsols	ferrallitic soils
(26) Histosols	peaty organic soils

7.9 Soil mapping

We have seen already that soils may be classified into major groups, groups and sub-groups. A

110

further subdivision is into *soil series*. These latter are differentiated by profile characteristics, chiefly lithological, that are not differentiated at subgroup level. They are usually named after places near which they are common or were first described (e.g. Evesham series).

It is very important to appreciate that until now we have been concerned with *conceptual soil classification*, which may differ from *soil mapping classification* or spatial soil classification. To understand the difference between these two it is perhaps best to visualize a hypothetical area of landscape of a size, let us say, of 100 m². Imagine that within this area 100 soil profiles have been described and the profile description notes taken away to the laboratory. If the profile description notes are sorted into piles according to soil series we might end up with a conceptual classification like this:

Pile 1 (series A)	Pile 2 (series B)	Pile 3 (series C)
35 profiles	30 profiles	30 profiles

Pile 4 (series D)	Pile 5 (series E)	
4 profiles	1 profile	

If we then went back to the original field area we might find that the soil series were distributed spatially as shown in Figure 112. It can be seen that some series overlap in their distribution. To produce a reasonable soil map with more or less discrete areas of the same sort of soil it is necessary

C	A	A	A	A	A	A	A	A	A
B	A	C	C	A	A	A	A	A	A
C	D	C	C	D	C	A	A	A	A
B	C	C	A	C	A	C	A	A	A
C	B	C	C	B	C	C	C	A	A
C	B	D	B	C	C	A	C	A	A
B	B	C	C	D	C	B	C	A	A
B	B	C	B	C	B	C	C	A	A
E	B	B	B	B	B	B	B	C	A
B	B	B	B	B	B	B	B	B	B

Figure 112 Hypothetical distribution of five soil series (A, B, C, D, E) in a 100m² area

to devise a new classification – a soil mapping classification. The lines between the mapping classification units (or *mapping units*) are shown in Figure 113. Each mapping unit will contain certain amounts of the particular series as follows:

mapping unit A: series A–100%, no other series

mapping unit B: series B–85%, C–11%, E–4%

mapping unit C: series A–7%, B–17%, C–66%, D–10%

The mapping units are named after the dominant included series. Thus, on a real soil map, Evesham soil mapping unit is dominantly Evesham series but may (and probably will) contain inclusions of other series. Not all soil memoirs and records state the precise amount of inclusions in percentage terms – most merely give an indication such as 'dominant', 'common', 'rare', etc. This is because to give a precise indication would involve very detailed sampling and checking, which is not always possible.

If a mapping unit contains more or less equal amounts of different series, or if no series contributes more than about 40 per cent, then the mapping unit is known as a *soil complex*. Soil complexes are commonly mapped, for example, on river floodplains where old river courses confuse the soil pattern.

Fortunately for those making maps, boundaries between soil mapping units often coincide with distinct boundaries in the landscape, like the edges of valleys and the crests of hills. This fact – which is not surprising when one considers the factors involved in soil formation – makes the drawing of the lines on the map a great deal easier. Soil mapping takes place in distinct stages, which will now be outlined.

Stage 1: Preparation – Before starting to work in the field the soil surveyor must assemble all the information available about the area in which he is to work. This includes geological maps, aerial photographs (if available) and papers on the geology, geomorphology and agriculture. Contact is made with local farmers and landowners and with agricultural scientists and advisers.

Stage 2: Field reconnaissance – The object of this is to provide background information on the entire area together with detailed studies in small sample areas. These small samples are chosen so that as far as possible they will give an impression of the main types of soil that are likely to be encountered when making the map. Usually small blocks of land or, alternatively, transects across the area are examined. Correlations with other similar soils elsewhere are made at this stage.

Stage 3: Legend construction – Following reconnaissance it should be possible to decide on soil mapping units for later detailed mapping. This stage is the most crucial to the final quality of the survey. The legend will include not only information on the different series within each mapping unit, but also information on the legend relationships of the map-

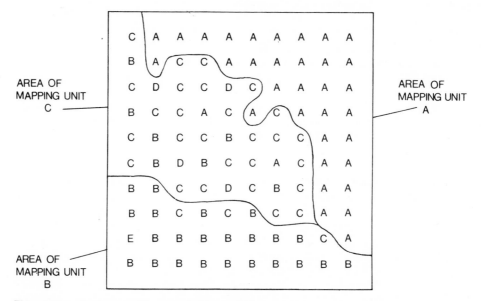

Figure 113 Soil map of the area in Figure 112

111

ping units. Each main series is described in a profile pit and samples taken for chemical analysis.

Stage 4: Detailed mapping – At this stage lines are drawn on a field map to correspond with mapping unit boundaries. To aid in this the surveyor will probably use a soil auger. Alternatively (or sometimes additionally) he may use a spade to make a small pit ('keyhole pit'). The scale of field map used depends on the ultimate scale of the published survey: usually a 1 : 10 000 field map is used for a published map of 1 : 25 000 whilst a 1 : 25 000 field map is used for a published map of 1 : 50 000. Some surveyors plot boundaries directly on aerial photographs which they carry with them in the field. Detail of recording depends on a number of factors, including the experience of the surveyor and the nature of the mapping unit variability. Some maps are made by detailed sampling schemes, whilst in others the sampling is more or less *ad hoc*. For a published map at 1 : 25 000 borings are usually made at a density of between thirty and sixty to the square kilometre.

Stage 5: Writing report – A detailed report of the soil map usually accompanies the published map. In Britain reports on the 1 : 63 360 are called 'soil memoirs', those on the 1 : 25 000 maps 'soil records', and those on other scales 'soil bulletins'. There is clearly a great deal of work in the fair drawing of the completed map.

Soil maps in Great Britain

Published soil maps of Great Britain are available at three main scales:

1:63 360 or one inch to one mile – Until the late 1960s this was the standard scale. Thirty one sheets have been published in England and Wales and about a further thirty sheets covering parts of Scotland. These maps are published on the 3rd Edition Ordnance Survey sheet lines, so as to provide direct comparability with Geological Survey maps.

1:25 000 – Because progress with the one-inch maps was proving to be rather slow, the system of soil mapping was changed in the late 1960s. The one-inch programme was terminated and a new series of 1:25 000 maps was started in England and Wales. The idea was not to provide a complete coverage of the country, but to map areas of particular geomorphological or agricultural interest and significance. To date (late 1983) about one hundred maps on this scale have been published.

1:250 000 – These maps now cover the whole of Great Britain. The maps show *soil associations* (groups of soils of different soil groups occurring in similar landscape situations).

7.10 Frameworks for research

For a long time soil study has consisted largely of observations of full soil profile descriptions. Although this type of observation is valuable in many cases, before starting field work it is important to establish exactly what sort of information is required and, perhaps even more important, exactly why the information is required. To enable one to think more clearly it is best to work within a framework of scientific enquiry. This involves setting up an *hypothesis* and formulating a field-work programme which *tests* the hypothesis. Following the acceptance or rejection of the initial hypothesis one is able either to formulate a *theory* or, alternatively, if the initial hypothesis has not been substantiated, set up a new hypothesis for subsequent testing.

Once a general outline of the research has been established the detailed arrangements must be worked out. The main steps in the research programme might be as follows.

1 *Hypothesis* – A general hypothesis might be 'that vegetation is related to soil type'. However, this is too general a hypothesis for it to be easily tested and one needs to formulate a *working hypothesis*. In formulating this hypothesis one must consider, in this case, two main questions:

a) what is meant by 'vegetation'?
b) what particular features of the soil are we referring to?

Obviously in this case the most straightforward approach is to look at certain aspects of soil and vegetation. The decisions as to which aspects to examine will depend to a great extent on the area being studied, and on the resources and skills of the research worker involved.

2 *Testing* – The statistical test or other method that is going to be used to test the relationship must be decided upon at an early stage. The detailed requirements of the test will determine the *size* of the sample. (It may be that the worker decides that a simple graphical representation of the results is all that is going to be produced, and worked towards. Whilst in the case of simple relationships these are sometimes very valuable, using such a technique does mean that less validity can be given to the con-

clusions drawn from such a graph or table – a very subjective element having entered the work.)

Decisions must also be made about *coding* the data. For example how are soil depth, soil stoniness to be estimated, recorded and presented for arithmetic analysis? Possible methods of doing this are:

soil depth: measured by auger to the nearest centimetre,
soil stoniness: percentage by volume at approximately 15 cm depth estimated by eye (this will involve excavating small 'keyhole pits'),

A sampling network must be set up in the field area and the data recorded for each of the sample sites.

3   *Formulation of theory* – From the results of the tests one can construct a theory about the relationships in the particular area studied. To see how far this was a substantial general theory one would have to retest the hypotheses elsewhere. It is important to understand that although there may be a relationship between two of these variables one cannot necessarily make a *causal connection*. One is not saying that the soil factors *cause* the vegetation distribution (microclimatic factors, for example, may be crucial, but merely that there appears to be some link between the two variables. There may, in fact, be a long causal 'chain' connecting the two variables, but further tests would be needed to establish the individual links. A possible basis for field testing of theories of soil formation is given in Appendix 4, where soil types are differentiated according to water flow on slopes.

Appendix 1

The analysis of soils for grain size (see section 2.3)

Method one – sieving

(The apparatus required may be purchased from A Gallenkamp and Co Ltd, Technico House, Christopher Street, London EC2B 2NA.)

APPARATUS NEEDED
Sieve stack appropriate to desired analysis, e.g. pan; 60 μm, 0·02 mm and 0·2 mm sieves (appropriate to differentiating clay and silt from sand sizes on the International Scale). Additional sieves can be used for more detailed analysis.
Sieve shaker
Wire and nylon sieve brushes
Selection of beakers
Pieces of paper larger than the diameter of the sieves
Weighing balance, capable of weighing to an accuracy of 0·01 g
Oven, capable of drying at 105°C
Desiccator
Electrical stirrer and flask
Calgon (sodium hexametaphosphate)

METHOD
1 Take a sample of roughly 150 g. Add 1 litre of distilled water.
2 Stir vigorously with the electrical stirrer, adding Calgon at the approximate rate of 2 g/litre. Stir for between 5 and 10 minutes. (Use less than 2 g rather than more in order to minimize foaming.)
3 To dry the sample, *either* leave to settle and decant and then place in oven at 105°C for 24 hours *or* put the sample direct into the oven at 105°C until the sample has evaporated to dryness. When in the oven stir occasionally to prevent caking. The first method of drying takes rather less time than the second. After drying in the oven cool in desiccator. A third method of drying is to air-dry the sample, which is slower but prevents caking. This is especially useful for soils with a high clay content which easily

harden on drying and may otherwise have to be broken up again with a pestle and mortar.
4 Weigh out 100.00 g of the dispersed dried sample. This is Weight 1 (W1).
5 Select and stack sieves, ensuring that the pan is at the bottom of the stack. Place on the shaker, insert the soil at the top and shake for 15 minutes.
6 Turn out the soil retained by each sieve on to separate sheets of paper. Brush each sieve upside down over the appropriate piece of paper using nylon brushes for the finer nylon sieves and wire brushes for the coarse wire sieves.
7 Pour each sample into an appropriate sized beaker and weigh to two decimal places (W2).
8 Weigh the beaker empty (W3).
9 Calculate the weight of soil in each size class (W4), thus:

$$W4 = W3 - W2.$$

10 The proportion of soil in each size class is usually expressed as a percentage by weight of the total sample and is therefore calculated thus:

$$\text{Proportion of soil in given size range} = \frac{\text{W4 for particular size range}}{\text{W1}} \times 100.$$

Method two – Sedimentation

APPARATUS NEEDED
Beakers, 250 ml, 500 ml, tall 600 ml
Evaporating basins for drying soil
Oven
Calgon (sodium hexametaphosphate)
Electrical stirrer and flask
Cylinders, tall glass 1 litre
Soil hydrometers, calibrated from 0–60 g/l
Thermometer

METHOD

1 Weigh out 60 g dry soil (W1). Sandy soils may be oven-dried at 105°C for 24 hours. Clay soils will have to be air-dried for 2–5 days (spread out on a tray to dry) or oven-dried at 30°C for 2–3 days. Otherwise they may set rock hard if baked at 105°C. Dry until constant weight is achieved (± 1 g on successive weighings).

2 Place in a tall 600 ml beaker with 500 ml distilled water and a small amount of Calgon (up to but not exceeding 1 g) and stir to dissolve Calgon. Transfer to stirrer flask and stir for 10 minutes, moving the flask round ensuring that all the structures are broken down into individual grains.

3 Choose a period when 6–8 hours is available (for details of time scale, see chart below). Pour stirred suspension into tall glass 1 litre cylinder. Add a further 500 ml distilled water, using some of this to rinse out the stirring flask. 60 g of soil are now mixed in 1 litre of water. Place hand over end of glass cylinder and invert approximately 30 times in a minute. Leave to stand.

4 After approximately 5 minutes take the first hydrometer reading (R1), using the chart below to determine the precise time. R1 is in g/l and as all the sand will have settled the reading is one of silt + clay in suspension.

5 After 8 hours take the hydrometer reading (R2). All the silt will have now settled and thus R2 represents the amount of clay in suspension.

6 Calculation:

   W1 = sand + silt + clay = 60 g.
   R1 = silt + clay, g still in suspension.
   W1 − R1 = sand, g settled out in first five minutes.
   R2 = clay, g still in suspension after 6–8 hours.
   R1 − R2 = silt, g settled out after 5 minutes but before 6–8 hours.

Express g of sand, silt and clay as a percentage of W1.

TEMPERATURE CHART

As the temperature increases the water becomes less viscous and the particles settle faster. Allowance has to be made for this in accordance with the chart below and care should be taken that the temperature is kept as constant as possible during the measurement. The settling cylinders should be kept away from sunlight or radiators and should preferably be placed in a constant temperature bath if one is available.

	Reading time	Temperature
R1	10 minutes	10°C
	5 minutes	18°C
	$4\frac{3}{4}$ minutes	20°C
	$4\frac{1}{4}$ minutes	25°C
R2	$8\frac{1}{2}$ hours	18°C
	8 hours	20°C
	$6\frac{1}{2}$ hours	25°C

Note: Taking the hydrometer reading may require practice. The hydrometer should be gently inserted into the liquid about half a minute before the required time and allowed to settle. The hydrometer should be kept as clean as possible and handled extremely gently as it is fragile.

Appendix 2

The estimation of organic matter content by loss on ignition

(see section 2.6)

Method one uses an oven capable of heating to 500°C and Method two uses a bunsen burner as the source of heat.

Method one

APPARATUS NEEDED
Small crucible for each sample
Oven capable of heating to 500°C (e.g. Gallenkamp Muffle Furnace)
Long tongs

METHOD
1 Oven-dry the soil at 105°C for 24 hours to remove moisture. Cool in a desiccator.
2 Weigh out 10 g of the cooled, dry soil (W1).
3 Weigh the crucible + soil (W2).
4 Place the crucible and soil in the oven at 500°C for 2 hours.
5 Remove the crucible from the oven with the tongs. Carefully inspect the sample. If unignited organic matter remains return sample to oven for a further half hour.
6 Cool the fully ignited sample in a desiccator.
7 Weigh the crucible and ash (W3).
8 Calculate the loss of weight of the soil sample:

W2 − W1 = weight of crucible (W4),
W3 − W4 = weight of ash (W5),
W1 − W5 = loss on ignition (W6).

W6 represents the loss in weight caused by the oxidation of organic matter at 500°C. This is usually expressed as a percentage of the original sample thus:

$$\text{Percentage of organic matter} = \frac{W6}{W1} \times 100.$$

Method two

The procedure is identical except that step 4 is replaced by setting up the crucible in a clay triangle over a bunsen burner, partially covering the crucible with a crucible lid. The crucible is heated until fuming ceases and then the weighing and calculations are carried out as above.

Appendix 3

The measurement of soil moisture content
(see section 2.7)

APPARATUS NEEDED
Container for soil (tin foil or specimen tube)
Oven capable of maintaining 105°C ($\pm 2°$)

METHOD
1 Collect a small sample (about 10 g) of soil in the field and carefully seal it immediately in the field to prevent moisture losses in transit. Suitable methods of sealing include wrapping in tin foil or placing in specimen tube sealed with Sellotape.
2 Weigh the soil and container complete (W1) (removing any Sellotape first).
3 Open up container and place container and soil in oven at 105°C for 24 hours.
4 Remove sample and container from oven and cool in a desiccator.
5 Weigh cooled container and sample (W2).
6 Discard soil and weigh clean container (W3).
7 Calculation:

W3 − W2 = weight of dry soil (W4),
W1 − W2 = moisture loss after heating in oven (W5).

Express the moisture loss as a percentage of the dry soil thus:
Percentage water that the mineral soil was

$$\text{holding} = \frac{W5}{W4} \times 100.$$

Appendix 4

Soil field study on a hillslope in Britain

A hillslope section is given below showing differentiation of soil and vegetation types according to hydrological conditions. This represents a generalised section which may be used as a basis for field soil study and shows a common arrangement of soils in a catena (see p.46) with slope-top podzols in well drained conditions, mid-slope brown earths and, at the base of the slope, gleys where drainage conditions are poor. Soils are thus differentiated because of drainage conditions: it is possible to test the validity of such a sequence during field project work – and if such a sequence is not found, then to discuss what other factors there are (e.g. parent material changes) which could have influenced soil formation.

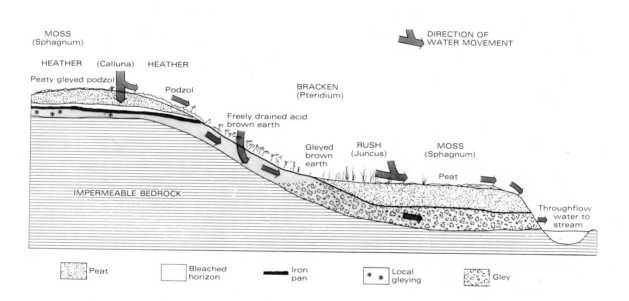

Water movement, soils and vegetation

Further reading

The following is a selection taken from the large amount of available literature.

A General texts
B Reading allied to specific topics

A   General texts

Brady, N C (1974), *The Nature and Properties of Soils,* Macmillan. A standard, comprehensive American text for detailed and advanced study.

Bridges, E M (1970), *World Soils,* Cambridge University Press. A lucid introduction to soil properties and soil types of the world. The colour illustrations of soil profiles are especially useful (and are available as a set of slides).

Bunting, B T (1972), *The Geography of Soil,* Hutchinson. A broadly useful text.

Curtis, L F, Courtney F M and Trudgill, S T (1976), *Soils in the British Isles,* Longman

Cruickshank, J G (1972), *Soil Geography,* David & Charles. A broad treatment of soil types and properties.

Donahue, R, *et al.* (1971), *Soils: an introduction to soils and plant growth,* Prentice-Hall. A detailed American book dwelling on ecological and agricultural viewpoints.

Duchaufour, P (1982), *Pedology,* George Allen and Unwin. A useful world-wide treatment with particular emphasis on genesis and classification.

Eyre, S R (1968), *Vegetation and Soils,* Edward Arnold. Of especial interest to geographers and ecologists. A very useful text dealing with processes and interrelationships on a world scale.

Faniran, A and Areda, O (1978), *Essentials of Soil Study,* Heinemann. Especial emphasis on tropical soils.

Fitzpatrick, E A (1971), *Pedology,* Oliver & Boyd. Intended for undergraduates. An individualistic soil classification is used which is confusing for the general student of soils.

Fitzpatrick, E A (1974), *An Introduction to Soil Science,* Oliver & Boyd. A useful introduction.

Pitty, A F (1978), *Geography and Soil Properties,* Methuen.

Russell, E W (1973), *Soil Conditions and Plant Growth,* Longman. A comprehensive, detailed advanced book. The standard British work on soil, dealing especially with the agricultural viewpoint. A necessary book for the serious advanced student of soils.

Townsend, W N (1973), *An Introduction to the Scientific Study of the Soil,* Arnold. Dealing with soil formation and especially with soil fertility, it is of especial value to the agricultural student.

White, R E (1979), *Introduction to Principles and Practice of Soil Science,* Blackwells.

B   Reading allied to specific topics

Soil texture and structure

Brewer, R (1964), *Fabric and Mineral Analysis of Soils,* Wiley.

Griffiths, J C (1967), *Scientific Method in the Analysis of Sediments,* McGraw–Hill.

Organic matter

Kononova, M M (1966), *Soil Organic Matter,* Pergamon.

Soil water

Hillel, D (1982), *Introduction to Soil Physics,* Academic Press.

Soil biology

Alexander, M (1961), *An Introduction to Soil Microbiology,* Wiley.

Burgess, A, and Raw, F (1967), *Soil Biology,* Academic Press.

Jackson, R M, and Raw, F (1966), *Life in the Soil,* Edward Arnold.

Philipson, J (1971), *Methods of Study in Quantitative Soil Ecology,* Blackwell.

Wallwork, J A (1970), *Ecology of Soil Animals,* McGraw-Hill.

Soil chemistry

Bear, F E (1964), *Chemistry of the Soil,* Van Nostrand/ Reinhold.

Hesse, P R (1971), *A Textbook of Soil Chemical Analysis,* Murray.

Ecosystems, water flow and plant ecology

Briggs, D J and Courtney F M (1985 in press). *Agriculture and Environment,* Longman.

Chorley, R J (1969), *Water, Earth and Man,* Methuen.

Gimingham, C. H. (1972), *The Ecology of Heathlands*, Chapman & Hall.

Soil management

Cooke, G W (1982), *Fertilizing for Maximum Yield*, Granada.
Hudson, N (1971), *Soil Conservation*, Batsford.
Kirkby, M J and Morgan, R P C, *Soil Erosion*, Wiley.
Smith, M J (1970), *Soil Mechanics*, Macdonald & Evans.
O'Riordan, T (1971), *Perspectives on Resource Management*, Pion.

Practical soil study

Andrews, W A (Ed.) (1973), *Soil Ecology*, Prentice–Hall.
Briggs, D J (1977), *Soil*, Butterworth.
Clarke, G R (1971), *The Study of Soil in the Field*, Oxford University Press.
Hanwell, J D, and Newson, M (1973), *Techniques in Physical Geography*, Macmillan.
Hodgson, J M (1974), *Soil Survey Field Handbook*. Soil Survey Technical Monograph No. 5. Harpenden: Soil Survey.
Hodgson, J.M. (1978), *Soil Sampling and Soil Description*, O U P.

Chapter six – additional references

In Chapter six the following items were referred to:

Avery, B W (1973), *Journal of Soil Science*, p.325.
Clayden, B (1971), *The Soils of the Exeter District*. Harpenden: Soil Survey Memoir.
Courtney, F M and Findlay D C (1978), *The Soils of Gloucestershire II*, Harpenden: Soil Survey Record.
Findlay, D C (1965), *The Soils of the Mendip District of Somerset*. Harpenden: Soil Survey Memoir.
Jarvis, M G (1973), *The Soils of the Wantage District*. Harpenden: Soil Survey Memoir.
Young, A (1979), *Tropical Soils*, Cambridge University Press.

Chapter seven – additional references.

In Chapter seven the following items were referred to:
Avery, B W (1980), *Soil Classification for England and Wales:* Soil Survey Technical Monograph No. 14, Harpenden: Soil Survey.
FAO (1974), *Soil map of the World*, Rome: FAO – Unesco.
USDA (1975), *Soil Taxonomy*, United States Department of Agriculture Handbook 436. Washington DC: Soil Conservation Service.

Sources

Figure 4 – Carson, M A, and Kirkby, M J (1972), *Hillslope Form and Process*, Table 9.4, p. 248.

Figure 7 – Adapted from data given in Deju, R A, and Bhappu, R B (1965), *Surface properties of silicate minerals*, N. Mex. Inst. Min. and Tech., State Bur. Mines and Min. Res. Circ. 82.

Figure 9 – As for Figure 4 plus data from Huang, W H, and Keller, W D (1972), *Organic acids as agents of chemical weathering of silicate minerals*, Nature, Physical Science, vol. 239, pp. 149–151.

Figure 11 – Adapted from Buckman, H O, and Brady, N C (1969), *The Nature and Properties of Soils*, Macmillan, Figure 1.4, p. 10.

Figure 54 – Modified from Young, A (1976), *Tropical Soils and Soil Survey*, C.U.P. p. 134

Figure 55 – Modified from Brady, N C (1974), *The Nature and Properties of soils*, Macmillan, Plate 2, facing p. 305

Figure 58 – Modified from Chorley, R J (1969), *Introduction to Fluvial Processes*, Methuen, p. 71.

Figure 61 – Modified from Catt J A (1979), Soils and Quaternary geology in Britain. *Journal of Soil Science, 30*, 607-642. p. 613.

Figure 62 – Modified from Brady, N C (1974), *The Nature and properties of soils*, Macmillan. p. 297.

Figure 64 – Modified from Mohr, E C J, F A Van Bar N and J. Van Schuylenborgh, (1972), *Tropical Soils*, Mouton, p. 225.

Figure 66 – Modified from Moss, R P (1968), *The Soil Resources of Tropical Africa*, C U P, p. 44.

Figure 76 – Modified from United States Department of Agriculture (1969), *Handbook*, 60.

Figure 107 Modified from Brady, N C (1974), *The Nature and properties of soils*, Macmillan, p. 351.

Figure 85 – After H M S O (1970), *Modern Farming and the Soil*.

Figure 90 – After Smith, M J (1970), *Soil Mechanics*, Macdonald & Evans, Figure 38.

Figures 91 and 92 – Both after Lambe, T W, and Whitman, R V (1969), Wiley, *Soil Mechanics*, Figures 9.4, 9.5 and 9.6, pp. 118–119.

Figure 110 – The Munsell Soil Color Company Ltd. The charts may be purchased from Munsell Color or from Tintometer Ltd (sole distributor in the U.K.).

Index

Figures in bold type thus, **22,** indicate the major reference of a group of references.